BEST SELLER ROMANCE

A chance to read and collect some of the best-loved novels from Mills & Boon—the world's largest publisher of romantic fiction.

Every month, four titles by favourite Mills & Boon authors will be re-published in the *Best Seller Romance* series.

A list of other titles in the *Best Seller Romance* series can be found at the end of this book.

Roberta Leigh

THE SAVAGE ARISTOCRAT

MILLS & BOON LIMITED
15–16 BROOK'S MEWS
LONDON W1A 1DR

*First published in Great Britain 1978
by Mills & Boon Limited*

© Roberta Leigh 1978

*Australian copyright 1978
Philippine copyright 1978
This edition 1984*

ISBN 0 263 74826 X

Set in Monotype Plantin 10 pt.
02–0884

*Made and printed in Great Britain by
Richard Clay (The Chaucer Press) Ltd,
Bungay, Suffolk*

CHAPTER ONE

'YOU'LL have to go to Peru instead of me,' Madame Delphine said, resting her dyed blonde head back on the pillows in her flower-filled room in the expensive nursing home off Harley Street. 'Dr Burton won't hear of me travelling anywhere until the end of the year, and you are the only one who can take my place.'

'But you've never even allowed me to go to our suppliers in Paris,' Vanessa protested.

'Paris and Peru are worlds apart,' Madame Delphine stated with truth. 'One is highly sophisticated and cut-throat and the other is primitive and—and——'

'Easily exploited,' Vanessa concluded.

'Not by *me*,' came the frigid answer. 'The Indians couldn't have been more delighted if I'd been their Saviour! And in a way I rather think I was. It isn't every day that someone comes along and buys up everything they've made.'

Madame Delphine's pale eyes glittered with pleasure as she recollected the dozens of sweaters, skirts, ponchos and lengths of vicuña and llama wool with which she had returned and filled her exclusive Mayfair boutique last November. But now the stocks were running low and had to be replenished; would already have been so had she not been struck down by a gall bladder infection necessitating the removal of said organ and a lengthy period of rest. Hence the suggestion —nay the order—that her trusted assistant go in her place.

In the ordinary course of events it was a journey Vanessa would have loved. But Delphine—no one knew her first name or if she had one—had returned from her journey there so full of the perils she had overcome, the hardships endured and the brilliant acumen needed to obtain all she had bought that Vanessa had marvelled at her employer's capability. All untrue, it seemed, if Madame was now to be believed. The trip could not have been easier, the travel better nor the Indians more helpful. There was nothing to it. A quick flight to Lima, a train journey across the Andes—stopping at vil-

5

lages en route—before returning to Lima and thence home.

But Vanessa still had her doubts. 'Why can't you write and explain you're ill and will fly out later?'

'Because none of the Indians can read—they're nearly all illiterate—and I don't have their addresses. I just know the villages where they live and the houses where I have to go.'

'It's a pity we don't have an agent there,' said Vanessa.

'The fewer people who know my sources the better. *Our* sources,' Delphine added slyly, reminding Vanessa of the carrot she had been dangling in front of her nose for the past two years: partnership in the boutique. 'The dress business is cut-throat enough without giving away all our contacts,' she continued. 'Being able to buy things no one else can get—and at such fantastically low prices—is the sort of thing one dreams of doing. You'll have to go there for me,' she reiterated. 'You know exactly what to get and I'll tell you what to pay. If you find anything else you like, I've enough respect for your taste to let you buy it.'

Vanessa knew that here was her chance to prove her worth, though she also knew she would never be able to get better prices than Delphine. From what the woman had said, the Indians were already practically giving their goods away.

'They've no overheads, of course,' Delphine had said half apologetically when Vanessa had first exclaimed at the inexpensiveness of the garments. 'They get the wool from their own llamas and sheep and they spin and weave it themselves. In some of the houses I visited, a loom was the only piece of furniture they had. It won't last, though.' This opinion had been given with a sigh. 'Tourists are already flocking there, and once that happens, prices go up. That's why we must get in quickly and buy everything we can.'

Eight days later, feeling like a pincushion from her assortment of inoculations, Vanessa boarded a British Airways flight to Lima.

'Take a few days off for sightseeing,' Delphine had said expansively, 'but don't be away for longer than two weeks.'

Vanessa forbore to say that the latter injunction made the first one impossible. The flight to and from Peru would take the best part of three days, and with long train journeys in the country itself, she would have her work cut out to do all her buying in the allotted time.

She thought of this again during the long hours that the aircraft droned over the South Atlantic and then across the dark green jungles of Brazil. Fourteen hours so far and one more to go. Her watch showed nine o'clock, though it would probably be nearer eleven before she had been cleared through Customs and Immigration and was in her hotel. She half smiled as she remembered her employer's barely concealed irritation when she had learned that her assistant had booked into the Gran Bolivar and not a *pension*.

'You'd have been far happier in a smaller place,' she had said. 'The Bolivar's too big and unfriendly.'

'It was the one *you* stayed at,' Vanessa had replied straight-faced, 'and you did tell me to follow your itinerary exactly.'

Gracefully Delphine had given in, but Vanessa had wondered—not for the first time—if she was wise to consider partnership with a woman who was penny-pinching where other people's comfort was concerned.

'Not far to go now,' a male voice murmured in her ear, and she turned to smile at Don Riversdale, who occupied the next seat to her.

He had been an excellent companion and had relieved the tedium of the flight by filling her in on many aspects of Peruvian life. Attached to the Trade Section of the British Embassy, he had been in Lima for three years and loved it.

'It has a pretty tight-knit social life,' he had informed her. 'Three million people live there, but there's only a few hundred wealthy ones—apart from visiting businessmen and tourists—so one tends to mix with the same crowd all the time.'

'That happens in London too.'

'But much more so in Lima,' he had replied. 'But the Creoles are very hospitable and give wonderful parties.' Seeing her questioning look, he had explained that Creole was the term given to Spaniards born in Peru, to differentiate them from those who had come from the Mother Country. 'You can always tell a Creole by his name,' he had added. 'They mostly begin with *al*.'

'What about the others?' she had asked, and had received a potted Peruvian history that had held her enthralled for a great part of her journey.

For centuries before it had been conquered by a handful of

Spaniards in the sixteenth century, Peru had been inhabited by many different, highly gifted peoples, though archaeologists had only comparatively recently started to learn about them. However, it was the Incas—who had ruled the country for three hundred years before the Spaniards conquered them—who provided Peru's most colourful history. From their capital Cuzco, high up in the Andes, they had dominated the land, building broad highways that would have done credit to the Roman Empire and constructing buildings which, even today, remained a source of wonder.

But it was the Inca gold and silver which had attracted Francisco Pizarro, and in 1531, with a handful of men, he landed in Peru and captured the reigning Inca. The brutality and deceit with which he did so did no honour to the name of Spain, but greed overcame principle and for nearly three centuries the Spanish Crown ruled there. Then in 1824 the same spirit of independence which had wrested North America from its European yoke brought freedom to Peru and it became a republic.

'Since then,' Don had explained, 'the country's had dictators, presidents and strong-arm generals, with the rich getting richer and the poor getting poorer. But ten years ago the military took over and things have started to improve. A huge land reform scheme is being carried out and many of the big industries have been nationalised.'

'There's still a great deal of poverty and sweated labour here,' Vanessa had commented, thinking of the reason for her own visit.

'Reform takes time. Half the population are illiterate Indians and one can't teach them a new way of life overnight. It will take years. In the meantime, hundreds of thousands of them pour into the cities looking for work, so you can imagine the way they live.'

'I'd rather not,' Vanessa had said, and had immediately felt guilty for wanting to close her eyes to unpleasantness. And she was the one who was critical of Delphine for wishing to avoid harsh reality!

'Look!' Don said urgently, and she brought back her mind to the present and her eyes to the window, where ahead of her a glitter of lights swept the Pacific coastline.

'You're lucky to get such a good view of Lima,' he murmured. 'From June to September it's usually covered with mist—except for the afternoon.'

'I know. When I asked at the Embassy what clothes I should bring, they told me lightweight woollens and a rain-coat.'

'It doesn't get all that cold,' he replied, eyeing her cash-mere suit, 'but it's hellishly humid. You should have come in the winter—that's the best time. The Humboldt Current stops it getting too hot.'

'Winter's a bad time for visiting the villages in the Andes,' she said. 'And since that's the only reason I'm here . . .'

'Spoken like a real business woman!' he smiled, and she smiled back at him, thinking how nice-looking and typically English he was, with his mid-brown hair and grey-blue eyes, his loose-limbed frame and erect bearing. It was a pity he was stationed in Lima and not London.

She peered through the window again, but though she knew the desert lay beneath her—the driest one in the world—it was too dark to see it, and instead she concentrated on the blaze of lights that was getting progressively brighter the nearer they came to the capital.

'Doesn't Lima ever go to sleep?' she asked.

'Not till late. People rarely dine before nine-thirty or ten.'

'It's still very Spanish, then?'

He nodded. 'In custom as well as religion. Even the Indians are Catholics. The Conquistadors brought the Incas to their knees and the missionaries and priests have kept them there!'

'At least they have a faith to believe in.'

'A lot of them would prefer food.'

She changed the subject. 'It's strange how Spanish ideas have continued to prevail. English ways didn't last in India. Once we pulled out, the Indians forgot us.'

'Because we educated them and trained them to take over. But here, the Spaniards only trained the people to be their servants.' He gave her a searching look. 'There's a lot of poverty in Lima, but it's considerably worse in other parts of the country. I'm not at all sure you should travel on your own.'

'My employer did,' she pointed out.

'She sounds a tough old bird.'

'She was a tough young one too!' Vanessa smiled. 'But then so am I.'

'I refuse to believe that!'

He studied her again, this time making it clear that he liked what he saw. But then most men did, for she was tall and slender, with shapely legs and patrician features topped by softly waving hair of a glorious shade of mahogany.

'I hope you'll be free to have dinner with me tomorrow?' he asked as the plane taxied along the runway. 'You'll want at least a couple of days here to plan your onward journey.'

'I did all that from London,' she explained. 'But I *am* free to have dinner with you tomorrow. I'm not leaving Lima until the day after.'

'Why not stay for the weekend and go on Monday? Then I'll have a chance to show you some of the sights?'

'It's a lovely idea,' she said wistfully, 'but I have to be in the mountain villages during the weekend. That's when they have their markets.'

The doors of the plane opened and the passengers began to file out. The Juan Chavey Airport had the feel of international airports the world over, and had it not been for the squat features and flat, impassive faces of the Indian porters, Vanessa might have thought herself in any other country.

Don took it for granted they would drive into the city together and, when they were both clear of Customs—which was sooner than most of the other passengers, owing to his having diplomatic immunity and exercising it for her benefit too—he ordered her luggage to be taken with his to a waiting taxi.

The car was an American one, as were many of the things that were imported into the country. It was too dark for her to get other than a fleeting impression of the countryside, though like so many suburbs which surrounded airports, this one was also sprawling, untidy and redolent of poverty. But over and above this was the sense of jungle which seemed to permeate everything; a strange feeling when one realised that the coastal area was predominantly desert.

'It's because of the vegetation,' Don explained when she remarked on it. He pointed to where tall grasses and rubbery leaves fought to get a foothold on the tarmac roads. 'You'll be even more aware of it during the day. Plants that you only see in pots or greenhouses in England you'll find growing on the sidewalks here!'

Vanessa was amused by the picture this conjured up, though the smile left her lips as the taxi skirted a vast garbage dump and she saw the tents and huts that were built upon it. 'People are living there!' she gasped. 'I can't believe it.'

'They're called *barriadas*—squatter settlements,' Don said soberly. 'You'll find them on the outskirts of nearly every big town. The Indians come down from the highlands looking for work, and when they can't find any, they make a living collecting garbage.'

'But they eat and sleep on it,' she burst out. 'Can't the government stop it?'

'They're trying; but it takes time and money. In Lima alone, more than a million people live like this. It can't be swept away overnight. Forget it,' he urged. 'It's not your problem.'

'It's humanity's problem,' she retorted, then stopped as she saw his face harden.

'It isn't that I'm unsympathetic,' he said, 'but I *am* at the Embassy and I do have to be diplomatic. So should you. Foreigners should be like the Three Wise Monkeys—see no evil, hear no evil and speak no evil.'

'Then I'd be like a U.N. delegate visiting an emergent state!'

He smiled without comment and allowed a few seconds to pass before he spoke. 'You'll see a lot of children without shoes too. Lima never gets cold and there isn't the same necessity to protect yourself against the weather.'

'Roads are rough.'

'The soles of their feet are probably rougher.' There was another silence. 'The children are also great beggars, but whatever you do, don't give them any money or they'll pester the life out of you.'

'Do all the Indians live on the garbage dumps?' she asked.

'Of course not. Those that have work live in adobe huts. They're made of mud and bricks.'

His pointing finger indicated a huddle of them on the roadside, but before Vanessa could make them out they were already giving way to larger homes, where the bricks were covered with plaster and intricately carved in old Spanish designs. It was too dark to see them clearly, and even when they skirted the beautiful Plaza de Armas, the main square of Lima, it was difficult to make out anything except the gleaming white buildings.

'We're only a few minutes from your hotel,' said Don. 'What are your plans for tomorrow?'

'Sightseeing and window-shopping. I want to see as many Peruvian clothes as possible to see if I agree with the styles Madame Delphine bought.'

'Peruvian clothes don't have any style. They all look the same!'

The taxi slowed down, then swung off the wide Avenida Nicolas de Pecola to turn into the brightly lit entrance of the Gran Bolivar.

'Would you like me to come in and see you settled?' Don asked.

She laughed and shook her head. 'I've a long trip ahead of me and I'll be all alone. Let me start getting used to it!'

Hoping that all her arrivals at the hotels into which she had booked would be as smooth as the reception that met her here —and pretty sure they wouldn't be—Vanessa signed in and was shown to her bedroom.

The boy who carried her luggage was squat and dark, with small black eyes and matt black hair. He spoke no English, but when Vanessa aired her few words of Spanish he answered immediately and followed it up with a wide smile that showed small, irregular shaped teeth. The smile did much to alleviate her feeling of alienness, and as soon as she was alone she unpacked and set out a photograph of her sister and two nieces, as well as the gold travelling clock that had been a twenty-first birthday present from her brother-in-law two years ago. The sight of some familiar things around her made her feel better and she went to the window and looked out at the lighted buildings.

They were not the massive skyscrapers of North America, but nonetheless seemed inordinately tall when one remembered the frequent earthquakes which shook the city. Still, like the skyscrapers of Tokyo, they had been designed to withstand tremors, and hoping there would be none while she was here, she rang room service and ordered a light snack.

The food, when it came, seemed like a plastic version of the real thing, but she was too tired to care and, as soon as she had eaten a couple of sandwiches and drunk a cup of milky tea, she went to bed and fell asleep.

She awoke to a hazy blue sky and an insistent knocking on her door. Sleepily she let in the waiter with her early morning coffee and stood by the window while she sipped it, debating whether it was warm enough to wear a silk suit.

Deciding it was, she dressed and left the hotel, heading for the reception travel agency to check that her flight to Cuzco was still in order. Then, with this done, she set off for a brief tour of the city.

Lima, like most towns of Spanish design, had been originally built around a plaza, and this one, which she had only glimpsed in the darkness last night, was seen—in the light of day—to be exceptionally beautiful. Though none of the buildings were very old—earthquakes having destroyed them —Spanish architecture was still much in evidence, with a preponderance of balconies, latticework and intricately fashioned arcades in old colonial style.

Just as it had been in Pizarro's day, the Plaza de Armas was the nucleus of the city. On one side of it the great Cathedral adjoined the Archbishop's Palace, while the President's Palace and the Municipal one faced each other. As Don had said, there were exotic shrubs and plants everywhere, and brilliantly coloured flowers grew along the wayside like weeds.

The avenues were wide, many of them a hundred feet across, and because she respected her feet, Vanessa did much of her sightseeing in a taxi; not one of the *collectivos* that took several passengers at a time and operated over specific routes, but a private one with a driver who spoke sufficient English to give her some kind of commentary on what she was seeing.

Modern Lima had swallowed up nearly all the fields that had once separated it from the port of Callas. Farm roads had become busy boulevards and residential suburbs had supplanted the fields. But the business and political heart of Lima was still bounded by the hundred and seventeen blocks which Pizarro had decreed when he had first set out his plans for his capital, and it was within this area—in a glass-walled coffin in the Cathedral—that one could see his mummified remains.

She had time only for a brief visit to a couple of museums and chose two which she thought might give her some idea of Inca tradition and design: the Museum of Art and a private one belonging to a wealthy Limeño, where she was enthralled by the ceramics, textiles and gold and silver objects.

After a snack lunch, taken during the surprisingly short break—the government having abolished the leisurely three-hour meal and siesta in order to stop people from returning home, thereby saving on petrol consumption—she asked her taxi driver to take her to the main shopping centre, where she paid him off and set out on foot to window-gaze.

In the four blocks between the Bolivar and Crillon Hotels she found a plethora of ethnic goods: alpaca wool sweaters, shawls, dolls, stuffed animals, Indian masks and beautifully made reproductions, in gold and silver, of Inca jewellery. There were prolific displays of leather-work with silver decoration and many wooden objects—caskets, frames and beautiful long low tables whose unusual woods came from the jungles of Peru. But the dresses in the shops were international in design and there was nothing distinctive enough to catch her eye. One did not come to Lima to buy St Laurent or Cardin!

Peruvian clothes were found only in shops that catered for tourists. As Don had said, they were all alike in style, relying for their attraction on their beautiful patterned borders and the texture of the fabric. How she longed to get the material in the raw and fashion it herself into something more appealing than the inevitable poncho or jacket. Many of the fabrics would also have made wonderful soft furnishings and drapes, and she wished it were possible to persuade Delphine to turn over part of her premises to this. But it was too faint a hope to be nurtured and she cast it out and decided to do some more sightseeing.

Despite the many new towering blocks and the fashionable crowds in the wide avenues, Vanessa was conscious of the past, due in part to the Spanish baroque churches so abundantly scattered through the capital, and the obsessive way in which plasterwork—aping ancient designs—was stuck on to the façade of many of the modern buildings. The private houses in the residential suburbs were equally guilty of this pretence, and the majority of them looked as if they had stood there long enough to have watched the Incas themselves march down to the coast. Yet they, like the rest of the buildings, had been built in the last hundred years, for devastating earthquakes had demolished those which had been built earlier.

By four o'clock Vanessa felt in need of refreshment. Her lunch of chicken and chips—chips seemed to be served with everything one ordered—had been tasteless and unsatisfying, and she went in search of a tea-room, finding one where she managed to get some delicious cream cakes and excellent coffee. The day was warmer than she had expected, though a cool breeze was now making itself felt, for Lima was five hundred feet above sea level, with rugged hills rising all around it. The sight of them reminded her of the journey still ahead, and her anticipation of it was tempered by fear. Quickly she chided herself for it. It was foolish to pay attention to Don. If Delphine could travel alone in the Andes, so could she.

Revived by her coffee, she debated whether to get another taxi and visit the harbour and a couple of beaches, then concluded that it was wiser to return to the Bolivar and rest. She was still unused to the time change and, tomorrow, would have to start getting used to a higher altitude as well. Slowly she wandered back through the main square, admiring the apricot glow brushed on to the buildings by the rays of the setting sun.

The rush hour was already beginning, though it was far less dense than in London. The mist was beginning to come in too, rolling up from the sea and making her skin damp. Glad of her jacket, she quickened her pace and was soon crossing the large lobby of her hotel. Don was not calling for her until nine and she had ample time for a leisurely bath and a letter to her sister. She was not sure what the postal service would be like once she left here, and thought it wiser to warn Joanna not to be worried if there was no word from her until she returned to London.

At eight-thirty she was ready and waiting for Don. Uncertain if he would be formally dressed, she was wearing black, knowing that in Lima, with its strong Spanish influence, such a choice would never be out of place. The lack of colour in her dress drew attention to her lustrous hair, which she wore in a centre parting and combed loosely down either side of her face. The simple style suited her tall slenderness and took on a newer sophistication when she put on hand-beaten silver earrings and a matching necklace.

Finding her room claustrophobic, she went down to the foyer, and the moment she did so, wished she had had the sense to remain upstairs until Don had arrived. She was the only woman on her own and was aware of many male eyes watching her as she sat down and tried to appear nonchalant. Everyone seemed to be with a party of people and there were far more foreigners than Peruvians, which she supposed was natural in a luxury hotel of this type. It was easy to distinguish the few Peruvians who were about, for they either had the pale skin and haughty features of the Spaniard, or the sallow skin and matt black hair of the *mestizo*—those with some Indian blood.

'I hope you haven't been waiting long?'

It was Don, every inch the attaché in a dark suit and navy satin tie. He seemed less familiar than the tousle-haired young man with five o'clock shadow on his chin with whom she had travelled halfway across the world yesterday, but when he smiled he was the man of her memory of him and she relaxed. It was surprising how glad she was to see someone she knew, even though it was only a brief acquaintance.

'I'm glad you came on time,' she replied. 'I was debating whether to go back to my room and wait for you.'

'You're quite safe as long as you're in the hotel,' he smiled, 'though I wouldn't advise you to wander round the streets on your own in the evening.'

'Is it dangerous?' she asked.

'Ruffians are the same no matter what country they come from. Indians of the old school would have been too proud to take anything that didn't belong to them, but the young ones are different.'

'If you're trying to frighten me,' she said lightly, 'you'll be pleased to know you're doing a great job! Don't forget I'll be travelling through the mountain villages, and if you tell me Lima's dangerous——'

'The villages are far safer than the cities,' Don interrupted. 'If any hands come out to grab you, it will only be from interest—not because they want to take anything.'

As he spoke he led her out of the hotel to his car: inevitably an American one.

'You too,' she remarked. 'At least you should keep the flag flying and drive British!'

'I would if I could get a British car here. But it's almost impossible. The American influence is very strong here,' he added. 'They supply all the technology.'

'All the smart clothes are foreign, too,' Vanessa added.

He chuckled. 'I like it when you talk about clothes. I have two sisters, but neither of them cares a jot what they wear. One's a vet who's always in jeans and the other's a doctor who only cares about the latest in stethoscopes!'

'I'm sure you're exaggerating,' she laughed. 'Anyway, I'm not interested in wearing clothes so much as creating them.'

'Another Chanel?'

'The one and only Vanessa Wayne.'

'What's stopping you?' he queried.

'Lack of money. It's a common failing among all students! That's why they usually join a wholesale house when they leave college. They get experience there and if their designs are good—and Lady Luck is looking their way—they might meet a buyer from a big store who'll give them a chance.'

'Is that the path you took?'

She nodded. 'I was just beginning to make my name when the man I worked for died. It was in mid-season and no one was engaging new designers. It meant I had to kick my heels for several months and when Delphine's offer came along, I took it. I was only going there temporarily, but I found I had a flair for designing unusual clothes for which women were prepared to pay unusually high prices!'

'So you've found your niche?'

'I think so. It depends whether or not I'm offered a partnership. That's why this trip is important to me. If I do well, Delphine will have to keep her promise.'

'If your main interest is in design, how come you're buying ready-made clothes?'

'Because Delphine is still the boss! If it were up to me, I'd use Peruvian materials to my own designs. Not modern ones,' she added hastily, 'but taking all the traditional ideas I've seen here and adapting them to Western requirements.'

'The Peruvian Government might be interested in that,' Don said slowly. 'They're anxious to bring industry into the villages. If you like, I'll arrange for you to meet someone who may be able to help you.'

'I'm not in a position to do as I want yet,' Vanessa replied. 'And at the moment, Delphine's happy to carry on the way she is.'

'Buying cheap and selling dear?'

'She doesn't put a gun to anyone's head,' Vanessa defended. 'I'm sure she's paying the prices she was asked.'

'I was teasing,' Don said hastily. 'I didn't mean you to take me seriously.'

The car slowed down and she saw they had left the business sector of the city and reached the suburbs, where a variety of large homes—some colonial in style and some ultra-modern —were all set in their own gardens.

'We're in San Isidro,' Don explained. 'It's one of the better residential districts and has some excellent restaurants. I hope you like seafood?'

'It depends what kind,' she said cautiously.

'Nothing too outlandish,' he grinned, and drew up outside a door bearing the name La Caleta.

Directly opposite was an almost identical-looking restaurant called La Barca, and further along the street, Vanessa glimpsed yet another.

'There's no shortage of eating places,' she exclaimed. 'I don't know why, but I assumed Peruvians preferred to eat at home.'

'On the contrary. They're extremely gregarious and do most of their entertaining outside. You're only invited to their homes if you're a close friend or part of the family.'

Although it was nine-thirty, the restaurant had not yet filled up and they were shown to an excellent table. Vanessa saw that her black dress was more than appropriate, since most of the women wore the same colour, though dark red appeared to be second favourite. Had she been put here without any pre-knowledge of where she was, she would have said she was in Madrid, though a second look might have modified her belief, for though the people had the dark hair and flashing eyes of the Spaniard, the hauteur was less evident. These colonials—no, these Peruvians, for no longer did they owe allegiance to Spain—were more boisterous in manner, and the intermingling of race with race was evident in hair being more matt than glossy, and features being flatter and less sharply defined.

A group coming in caught her eye; not because they were greatly different from the rest but because of the height and appearance of one of the men. He was the tallest, most supremely confident-looking male she had seen. He was too far away for her to discern his face, but his skin was darker than his compatriots'—due either to Indian blood or the hot sun, she was not sure which—and his hair had an unusual lustre, almost as if a veil of gold had been draped over the silky blackness. As she watched, he turned to one of the female members of his party—strange how she knew instinctively that he was the host—and guided her towards a large table on the far side of the room where, seated, he was no longer in her vision.

'Some of the men are very striking,' she commented.

'That's what I think about the women!' Don responded, and they both laughed and set about ordering their meal.

They began with grilled *chorus*—large, fat mussels sprinkled with parsley and garlic—and followed this with *ceviche*, uncooked white fish marinated in lemon juice, hot peppers, corn, sweet potatoes and onions. The mixture of flavours was unusual and Vanessa was careful to avoid biting into the peppers, which she found too hot for her palate. But the white wine that accompanied the dish was locally produced and excellent, as was the sweet avocado jelly with which they concluded their dinner.

Don refused to let her talk about her work, almost as if he sensed her increasing nervousness at the long journey ahead of her, and instead talked of his own, which seemed to be acting as liaison between visiting British trade delegations and the Peruvian Government.

'At the moment,' he explained, 'I've a group here trying to stock-pile fertiliser because the anchovy catch was so good last year.'

She looked at him blankly. 'What do anchovies have to do with fertiliser?'

'The little darlings are made into it! Millions of them are

caught off this coast. They're diverted here because of the Humboldt.'

'An underwater traffic warden,' she quipped.

'A benevolent one as far as the Peruvian economy is concerned.' Don was serious. 'It brings them in a fortune.'

'For the Government or for a few private companies?'

'They share it. There are about a dozen Creole families who control most of the private wealth. They made huge fortunes years ago through cotton and cattle, and they're still in a position of power.'

'What about the gold and silver mines?'

'Lots of them are worked out. I've a book at the office describing what Lima looked like a few hundred years ago. Every building glittered with gold like a Christmas cracker.'

'What happened to it?' she asked.

'An earthquake. Lima was practically destroyed.'

'But not the Spanish Grandees,' she murmured.

'It would take more than an earthquake to dislodge *them*,' Don agreed. 'But they do a lot of good. Their haciendas run profitably and their workers are well cared for. Some of the owners even give them a share of the profits.'

'Benevolent despots,' she retorted.

'You get despots in the Kremlin too,' said Don. 'If you could wangle an invitation to a hacienda for a weekend, you'd know the meaning of living like a queen.'

'I'd loathe it,' she said firmly. 'I'd keep thinking of the Indians and their shanty towns.'

He sipped the last of his wine. 'Are you definitely leaving Lima tomorrow?'

'Yes. I'm flying to Cuzco in the morning. I'll stay there overnight and then start visiting the villages where Madame Delphine is expected.'

'Transport's rotten,' he warned. 'You should try to hire a car and driver.'

'I will if I can.' She saw his anxious expression. 'I'll be back in about a week.'

'If you aren't, I'll come looking for you.'

'Give me a few days' leeway,' she said hastily. 'If transport's as bad as you say, it might take me longer than I expect.'

Don rested both arms on the table and regarded her. 'Beats

me why a beautiful girl like you isn't married. I can't believe it's lack of opportunity.'

'Call it lack of desire,' she answered.

'You're not frigid,' he said instantly. 'Not with that mouth.'

'I meant desire for marriage,' she corrected.

'Meaning that you're open to other suggestions?'

She bit back a sigh. How predictable men were! 'No,' she said, 'I'm not.' She looked at her watch. 'I've an early flight, Don. Do you mind if we go?'

'You're not annoyed with me, are you?' he asked at once. 'I wasn't trying to . . . What I mean is, I wasn't——'

'You were and I'm not!' she said with a faint smile. 'Don't apologise for trying; it's all part of twentieth-century living!'

'And you'll let me see you again?'

She nodded, thinking suddenly how immature he was and how much older he made her feel. But he was in command of himself again when he left her at the Bolivar, and he made no attempt to kiss her goodnight or suggest she change her mind and remain in Lima over the weekend.

'I'll be waiting for your call when you get back,' he said. 'You have my number at the office?'

'And I'll use it,' she promised, and quickly retreated to the safety of the elevator.

In her room she undressed and wandered round aimlessly for several moments. Her reflection in the mirror seemed to be that of a stranger, and she frowned at the slender figure topped by an almost too heavy weight of hair. Tonight several men had eyed it as if eager to put their hands on the silken mass, and she wondered if it seemed more striking because she was in a country where jet black hair was so predominant. She smiled, her mouth curving upwards to show even white teeth. In repose she exuded a quality of stillness, but with humour she took on a more tempestuous personality. Even her eyes became a brighter blue. To test the theory she set her mouth tightly and frowned. Yes, her eyes were definitely darker now: almost the colour of lapis lazuli. She smiled and they lightened again.

Turning away from the mirror, she began to repack her clothes. Judicious thought had enabled her to travel with only one case, and she blessed the invention of man-made fibres. She might be going to a part of the country where people lived the way their forefathers had done since civilisation began but, by courtesy of Courtaulds, she would remain crease-resistant and clean.

CHAPTER TWO

THE jet Fokker of Aeroperu made short shrift of the journey to Cuzco, and one that, in earlier times, would have taken five days by bus and train, was accomplished in an hour.

Staring down at the hard-edged ridges of the Andes, with their deep crevasses through which flowed the many tributaries of the two great rivers of the region, Vanessa felt like a microcosm in space. The desert plains had been left behind and for as far as the eye could see, the Andes reared into the sky: the craggy spires of the Southern Americas.

Fifty minutes out from Lima the jet started to lose height and the land below became more discernible. Cuzco, the ancient capital of the Incas, lay in a plain, at an altitude of more than eleven thousand feet. The surrounding area of mountains was heavily cultivated, their terraced slopes providing food and a living for the people who had lived here for centuries.

The seat belt light flashed on, and almost as Vanessa fastened it, they were approaching the runway. Stepping out of the plane, she was instantly aware of the cold sharpness of the air, despite the blue sky and bright sunshine. No wonder she had been warned to take warm clothing with her no matter what the season.

Cuzco itself was a short taxi ride from the airport, and she shared it with a portly man who spoke halting English and told her he was here on business.

'You *turista, si*?' he enquired.

'No. I'm here on business too.'

'You find time visit Machu Picchu,' he stated and, at the shake of her head, gesticulated broadly, which seemed to be a Peruvian custom, as was the one of shaking hands with everyone on meeting and leaving them. 'You cannot come so far and not see old Inca city. Is eighth wonder of world!'

'I know,' she agreed. 'But I don't have the time.'

To forestall further discussion she stared through the window. Even a fleeting glimpse of the town showed her the strong intermingling of Indian and Peruvian culture; where else could one find beautiful Spanish colonial churches whose foundations were walls of Inca origin?

The business centre of Cuzco was also a mingling of old and new, and created its own vivid pictures: a bowler-hatted Indian woman squatting on the kerbside to sell her wares next to a parked jeep; a sober-suited man striding alongside a llama that was being pulled by a poncho-clad Indian—descendant of the very Incas who had built this city.

The taxi stopped at the Plaza de Armas—far smaller than the one of the same name in Lima—to let out the Peruvian man and then drove Vanessa the short distance to the Turista Hotel, where she was staying. It was small and staffed mainly by Indians, except for the *mestizo* clerk at the desk who welcomed her and had her shown to her room.

It was not yet nine o'clock and, anxious to visit the market early, she washed in the small bathroom off her bedroom and then went down the two flights of stairs in search of a reviving cup of coffee. The dining room was deserted—most visitors having long since departed on their excursions, if the untidy state of the tables was anything to go by and, deciding to forget about a drink, Vanessa too set out.

To her disappointment the market place was small and nowhere near as colourful as she had anticipated. Nor was there any of the laughter and chatter one associated with crowds at such a gathering place. The Indians here were a silent race and their faces remained devoid of expression regardless of the emotion they felt.

Following her employer's instructions, she spent most of her time in the numerous little shops to be found in the cobbled alleyways, and discovered an amazing variety of goods. But here too the proprietors were Indians, who watched her impassively and made no effort to sell their wares. But when she picked up a hand-embroidered shawl and exclaimed aloud at its excellent workmanship, the owner of the shop immediately hurried into the back and returned with several more in different colours. From then on Vanessa took no notice of the solemn faces, and when entering a new shop, smiled and enthused over all she saw. This action worked wonders and goods and articles were brought to her that were not otherwise on display.

Anxious to find something that Delphine had missed, Vanessa searched diligently, but apart from lovely lengths of vicuña—a superfine wool as soft as cashmere and as light-weight as mohair, yet warm and hardwearing—she saw only a repeat of the garments they were already stocking. She really must persuade Delphine—or someone else, if her employer refused—to sell Peruvian materials by the length. If only she could afford her own shop and had no need to beg people to follow her fashion hunches!

She was crossing one narrow street to get to another row of small shops when the scene around her seemed to turn upside down. The austere and beautiful mountains that ringed the horizon were suddenly revolving beneath her, while the cobbled streets were coming up towards her head. She staggered and clutched out for support, looking up with relief when her hand was taken by a middle-aged woman who was walking along with another of similar age.

'Anything wrong, honey?' The accent was American and Vanessa gave a gasp of relief.

'Thank goodness you speak English! It's just that I'm giddy.' She swayed and clutched more tightly at the hand. 'I suppose I should have had breakfast when I got here.'

'You've only just arrived?'

'A few hours ago.'

'That's why you're ill. You've got *soroche*. You'd best go back to your hotel and lie down.'

'Oh dear!' Vanessa was dismayed. To be ill here was the last thing she had banked on.

'It isn't serious,' the woman assured her. 'It's altitude sickness. Didn't anyone tell you not to rush around as soon as you got here? If you go to sleep for the first few hours, your body gets acclimatised to the height.'

Irritated that no one had warned her of this—surely Don or Delphine could have done so—she murmured her thanks when the American woman offered to take her back to the Turista, and gratefully allowed herself to be bundled into a taxi and driven the short but steep distance to the hotel, where she went to her room and collapsed on the bed, convinced she would never get up again.

Two hours later she awoke from a deep sleep feeling her normal self and once more set out for the shops. Again she felt a deep urge to buy lengths of fabric instead of ready-made garments, and vowed to return to Cùzco after she had visited the outlying villages whose names Madame Delphine had given her. The wonderful alpaca rugs were also tempting, for she could visualise them as wall hangings or, backed on to a heavier fabric, used as floor rugs. Indeed the more she saw the more convinced she became that a little innovation could greatly expand the market for Peruvian goods.

As soon as the sun began to sink behind the craggy, snow-capped peaks of the Andes, it became bitterly cold, and she returned to the hotel to shower and change before going in search of dinner. Don had warned her that the food at her hotel was poor and had suggested she go to a restaurant called the Balkan. But now that she was actually here, and remembering her earlier giddiness, she considered it wiser to take things easy, and settled for the Turista dining room and an inadequate meal poorly served.

By nine-thirty she was in bed, exhausted by the altitude and slightly desolate at the knowledge that she was thousands of miles from home. Peru had an alien quality that made it seem as if it were much more than halfway round the world from England; it was almost as if she were on another planet. It was a disquieting thought with which to court sleep, and she forced herself to think of fashion and what clothes she could design from the coarsely woven wools she had seen. She was working on the intricacies of a bias-cut skirt when she fell asleep, and awoke to find bright sunshine filtering into her bedroom through the partly drawn curtains.

The light brought with it a revival of her spirits, and though it was barely six o'clock, she dressed and went down to breakfast. This too was a disappointing meal, with poor coffee—for which there was no excuse since Peru grew its own—and slightly rancid butter on stale rolls. Reminding herself she was not here on a gourmet holiday, she donned a thick-knit cardigan over her sweater and slacks and set out for the square and the buses.

It seemed that several hundred Indians had the same intention, and feeling as though she were in a rugby scrum, Vanessa managed to squeeze herself on to a single-decker bus that was going to the village of Pizoc. Though it was built to carry only forty passengers, nearer a hundred and fifty squashed themselves in, more if one counted the livestock in their baskets and the black-eyed babies slung on the backs of their colourfully dressed mothers, whose long robes hid their unwashed bodies but could not disguise the smell of them.

Not counting on getting a seat, Vanessa was not disappointed, and she clutched on to the rail for the length of the two-hour journey. The roads were muddy, despite this being the dry season, and pot-holes abounded, so that by the time the bus drew to a stop in the village square, she felt as if every bone had been dislodged from its socket.

The market was in full swing and appeared to be the centre from which all business radiated. But she had other tasks to fill before strolling around here, and she set off in the direction of the adobe houses. Without benefit of a covering layer of plaster, their mud bricks were visible to the eye and looked so primitive that she did not relish the prospect of having to enter them.

She paused outside the largest one. It was here that Delphine had told her Minca lived: an Indian woman who had promised to have several dozen ponchos ready for collection. No one was visible and she stared at the narrow door, reluctant to enter uninvited.

She was still debating what to do when an old woman rounded the corner. Her long white skirt was topped by a thick dark jacket, and her head was covered by a hard-rimmed hat resembling a bowler. She was smoking a pipe and Vanessa tried not to breathe in the fumes as, in careful Spanish, she pointed to the hut and asked if it was Minca's home. Only as she uttered the name Minca did the other woman react, replying to her in a spate of incomprehensible language which Vanessa took to be either Quichuan or Aymara, the two principal languages spoken by the natives of the Sierra region. She shook her head to indicate that she did not understand what was being said and the woman said 'Minca', pushed at the door and urged her forward.

Bending double to avoid hitting her head on the lintel, Vanessa stepped into a circular room. The only opening was the door through which she had come and since this was also the only source of light, an oil lamp burned on a small wood table at the far end. Several alcoves opened out from this central room and she glimpsed colourful rugs and wall hangings. Though primitively furnished, everything was spotlessly clean; no mean achievement without sanitation and running water. A plump woman came forward to greet her, and Vanessa took out a photograph of Delphine from her bag and haltingly explained that she was here as her employer's representative to buy the garments that had been made for them.

Blankness met her request and the two women muttered to each other and then fell silent. More slowly Vanessa repeated what she had said, but it only resulted in a rapid shake of Minca's head and a sigh which indicated that no ponchos were available.

'You must have made *some* in the last four months!' Vanessa exclaimed.

There was a noticeable hesitation, and remembering Don's injunction always to be polite and friendly, Vanessa gave both the Indians a warm smile and then sat on the only chair available. At least it would show she had no intention of leaving until she had seen what she had come for, even though there appeared to be some problem about her buying anything. Above her head the two women spoke again, then Minca went into the furthest alcove and emerged almost at once with an armful of ponchos.

'They're lovely,' Vanessa said instantly, but as she went to touch them, Minca drew back in alarm, making it clear they were not for sale.

Accepting defeat, Vanessa left the house, the older woman shuffling along beside her, talking unintelligibly in a cracked voice.

Realising she had found herself a companion during her stay here, Vanessa gave her the names of the two other Indians she had come to see, and was delighted when the woman nodded vigorously and led her to the outskirts of the village and two smaller adobe houses.

But here too she was met with the same refusal to sell, and

since one of the women could speak a little Spanish, Vanessa was able to learn that all the women in Pizoc had been forbidden to sell their garments to foreigners.

Had she been able to converse with the women in their own language, Vanessa would not have accepted defeat so easily, but as it was, she returned to the square and boarded the bus which was leaving for the next village.

This one was smaller than Pizoc and built halfway down a terraced mountainside, with the adobe huts clinging stubbornly to the sides. There was no village square, but where the bus parked there was a congregation of people, their wares set out on the ground in front of them, some directly on the earth and some on rugs.

Boldly Vanessa approached a woman sitting on a small mat beside a large bundle of sweaters made of rough wool that resembled hessian. Its brownish colour was almost the exact shade of the woman's skin, but the eyes watching her were dark brown and alert, and glinted with pleasure as Vanessa indicated she liked what she saw and wished to make a purchase. It was only when she went to gather up the entire stock that the woman's friendly attitude changed, and with a violent shake of her head that nearly tumbled the high-crowned bowler hat she wore, she made it clear she had changed her mind and did not wish to sell anything.

Vanessa did not argue. The attitude of the women in Pizoc had already warned her that something was going on, and to meet it again in another village confirmed this belief. Wondering if there was some religious or superstitious reason why the Indians did not wish to sell their goods to her, she decided to return to Cuzco and talk to a priest; it might give her an explanation and help her to find a solution. If it didn't, she would try to contact Don at the Embassy in the morning.

During the long and tiring journey back to Cuzco, she also debated whether to telephone Madame Delphine, but finally decided it would be better to find out what was causing the problem before making her call.

Once back in her hotel her despondency lessened. There was nothing like a bath and a warm room to improve one's mood and she could almost make herself believe that what had happened in the two villages today was of no significance. It seemed alarmist to talk to anyone until she had made sure she was not exaggerating. Tomorrow she would go to the villages around Lake Titicaca. This was where she would be doing the bulk of her buying, and only if things went wrong there would she then ask for advice.

Eight o'clock the next morning found Vanessa gazing in wonderment at one of the most ornately decorated old trains she had ever seen. With its intricately carved woodwork, brass handles and fittings and shiny leather seats that looked to be more suited to crinolines than jeans, it could have shunted straight out of a Victorian lithograph.

However, gracious though it looked from the platform, once aboard it was seen to be ramshackle, with peeling paint, holes in the woodwork and rents in the leather. But neither holes nor rents were visible once the train started its eleven-hour journey across the high Andean plain to Puno, for every inch of it was covered with livestock and children, people and packages.

Yet packed though it was, every wayside halt brought with it another influx—always of Indians—who clambered aboard and proceeded to try and sell their wares to the passengers. The goods they offered were similar to those found in the markets; jewellery, llama fur jackets in hideous styles and toys made of a type of balsa wood, which were colourfully painted and tempting to buy. There were also numerous garments made of leather and the ubiquitous ponchos and sweaters, though these were too roughly made for Vanessa to consider buying them as an alternative to the ones she had been unable to get yesterday.

She was amused at the haggling that went on between buyers and vendors, though saddened when she realised that the initiative always lay with the buyer. He had all the time in the world in which to bargain—the eleven hours it took to reach Lake Titicaca, in fact—while the Indians were anxious to make their sales as quickly as possible, since every passing moment took them further and further from their home and, once they left the train, they faced a long walk back on foot.

Even if one paid the original asking price, all the goods offered were extremely cheap, and her sympathies lay entirely with the Indians who, even from the little she had seen of them, struck her as a proud race of people living at subsistence level. Yet the ancestors of these same Indians had once been the masters in a country where they were now only second class citizens.

Angered by the way one haughty-looking man was haggling over the price of a furry toy animal, she bought it herself for the exact asking price, then immediately became the target for all the other Indians, who stuck their trays in her lap and stared at her with impassive faces and intent black eyes. Unwilling to laden herself, she debated whether to buy some of the food that was for sale. At least once she had eaten it, she wouldn't have to carry it. There seemed to be an interesting selection, from various kinds of flat maize cakes to *tamales*—corn with hot peppers wrapped in banana leaves— and *picarones*, which looked like doughnuts but which her plump neighbour informed her were made from yuca, a tropical root vegetable grown in the valleys that lay between the high mountains, and was mixed with flour and eggs and fried in fat.

'You should buy enough for a couple of meals,' the woman added, her poor Spanish showing she was more accustomed to speaking a local dialect. 'The Indians will be leaving the train completely in another hour and you won't be able to buy anything to eat or drink until you get to Puno.'

The prospect of travelling for so long without food was all the persuasion Vanessa needed, and she bought enough *picarones* and *tamales* to sustain her till she reached her destination, as well as a large bottle of mineral water. The food might not win awards for hygiene, but it looked good and it smelled even better. Apart from which, no one around her looked as if they were worried about getting food poisoning!

She had cause to bless her neighbour's kindly advice many times during the long and tiring day, and wondered crossly why Delphine had not thought to warn her that most trains in Peru did not have restaurant cars. But then Delphine rarely thought of anyone else's comfort other than her own.

Slowly the old train chugged its way asthmatically across the high, cold, windswept plateau, stopping at small townships to let one or two people disembark. There was little colour in the scene. Greyness predominated and the vast mountain ranges brooded sombrely around them, their tops capped with eternal snow and rimmed by rain clouds.

This was the land where llama, vicuña and alpaca roamed;

lovely creatures whose name Vanessa knew only because of the value of their wool or fur. It was a disquieting thought until she reminded herself that wool was obtained without having to kill the animal which provided it.

Hopefully she stared across the landscape for a sight of these unusual creatures, but all she saw was a scattering of stone huts; homesteads of the Aymara and Quechua Indians who took care of these herds and scratched an extra few *soles* from cultivating the knobbly potatoes she had seen in the various market places she had visited.

At rare intervals she glimpsed larger stone houses, each one a centre for a privately owned hacienda that, so her talkative neighbour informed her, would probably cover tens of thousands of acres.

'They produce the finest wool in the world,' the woman said proudly.

'Vicuña wool is known to be the best,' Vanessa agreed.

'I mean sheep's wool! They are a very special breed here. You should look out for it.'

Vanessa murmured that she would, then studied her neighbour with more care. Her hair was dark as a raven's wing, though the lined face gave indication of middle-age. But the eyes were bright and alert as a girl's and were studying her with equal curiosity.

'Do you own a *hacienda*, *señora*?' Vanessa asked.

There was a throaty chuckle. 'I would not be travelling by train if I did. I would be on an aeroplane! No, no, *señorita*, I am housekeeper on a big *estancia* and my employer has returned to Lima. I will be joining him there in a week. *He* is the one who owns the *hacienda*.'

Vanessa was confused. 'Isn't an *estancia* the same thing?'

'In Peru, an *estancia* means a large estate. But it can be anywhere. And my master has his home outside Lima.'

'Doesn't he live on his *hacienda*?'

'No, no. Señor Mandola likes the bright lights and much society. He has a manager who takes care of it for him. But he is always complaining that it does not bring in enough money.' Arms rose expressively. 'But what would you? A manager will never take the same care as an owner. To him it is just a job. One day I think the Government will take it over, and then Señor Mandola will have nothing to complain about!'

'Does that happen often?'

'Not often enough. Too many rich men have big properties that they do not care about.'

Vanessa could sympathise with the woman's point of view. A well-run *hacienda* meant better conditions for its workers. She was on the verge of saying so when she decided to keep silent. She was a visitor here and it did not behove her to make comments—critical or otherwise—about the country. And certainly not in a public place.

Digging her chin into her jacket collar, she stared through the window.

They were now deep in the heart of the Andes. The temperature was affected not so much by the distance they travelled as by their altitude, and peering down into some of the valleys, five and six thousand feet below her, she was astonished to glimpse luxurious vegetation, often highly coloured and tropical. To her surprise there was even a discrepancy between one side of a valley and the other, with eastern slopes grassy and the western ones lush with a jungle-like growth.

As the sun sank lower and the sky darkened, she could no longer make out the view, though she knew they were still crossing the *alto-plano*—the vast flat basin of the high Andes. It was in this basin that lakes and swamps sprang up between low-lying hills, and the largest lake of all—Titicaca—was her final destination before she returned to Lima.

Titicaca. Even the name seemed to come from another world, and she was once more uneasily aware of how alien this land was; worse still, that she was a comely young woman travelling on her own.

She knew that interested glances had been directed her way by several of the men who swaggered along the corridor past her compartment, but she had pretended not to see them, and from time to time had deliberately engaged her plump neighbour in further conversation, hoping to give the impression that she was not without friends.

Darkness was now complete and like a glow-worm the train crawled its way upwards. The altitude was too high for trees and only coarse grasses and clumps of *yareta*—a wood shrub which a fellow passenger told her was used as fuel by the Indians—could be seen.

The thought of warmth was not as enticing as the thought of food, for she had long since eaten all she had bought and wished she had taken twice as much. Her neighbour offered her a bar of chocolate, but she politely declined it, and listened enviously as the rest of the occupants of the carriage noisily munched and crunched their way towards Puno.

Eleven hours after leaving Cuzco, they arrived at this little capital, and stepping out of the train and meeting the force of the wind, Vanessa felt as if she had come to Siberia. Hurriedly she sought a taxi—the inevitable dilapidated American car which barely managed to go. Uncertain if the driver spoke Spanish, she had written down the name of her hotel, and he nodded and rattled her through the narrow streets at what seemed breakneck speed, though it could not have been more than twenty miles an hour and only seemed fast because of the sharp lurching of the car and its poor suspension.

Happily, her hotel was far less antiquated. It was a two-storey building of stone and concrete, with a high, steep roof and an inside balcony encircling the first floor. The furniture looked as if it had been left there by the Spanish Conquistadores, being of black carved wood, rustic in design and massive in size. The Indian desk clerk spoke English with a strong American accent, though the boy who showed her to her room spoke only his own dialect, which she could not follow.

Her bedroom was on the second floor and overlooked an inner courtyard which ensured her some quietness. Here too the furniture was massive and dark, though the small shower-room which led off it was pink-tiled and chromium-fitted. It was a reassuring sign of civilisation and she took advantage of it to wash away the grime of her long journey before going down to dinner—another poorly cooked meal that tasted as if it had come out of a package.

Afterwards she returned to her room. Had it been earlier she would have tried to visit some of the women on her list of names, but she was sure they were already asleep; primitive people geared their hours to the daylight and would, by now, be halfway through their night's rest. Deciding to follow suit, Vanessa went to bed, first opening her window a chink to let in some air. Even this proved too much, and an hour later she awoke shivering with cold and was forced to close it again.

It took her a long time to get back to sleep and it was past eight o'clock before she stirred. It was a grey day and cool, but then it was never above the fifties at this altitude and she was glad of her trousers and sweater.

After a breakfast of tinned orange juice, rubbery omelette and lukewarm coffee, she set out to see Maria—the first name on her list. The address led her to a small stone house. It had a narrow slit for a door and a steeply thatched roof of reddish tiles. Less nervous than when she had visited Pizoc, she went straight in and was brought up short by the sight of a young woman standing in a corner breast-feeding a baby, and an older woman, who could have been the grandmother though she was not above forty, giving some kind of gruel to a couple of toddlers sitting on the floor. It was the older woman who answered to the name Maria.

'She's quite bright,' Delphine had said, 'and she speaks fairly decent Spanish—which is a blessing—so you'll be able to make yourself understood. She's the most marvellous knitter and has promised to have at least thirty sweaters for me. She has masses of children and probably has them all working for her!'

But once again Vanessa found her employer's hopes unjustified, for Maria produced only three sweaters and these at a far higher price than Madame Delphine had originally paid. Vanessa was dismayed. Had she been her own boss she would have given the price asked, for there would still have been no need to increase their London prices; at the five hundred per cent profit the boutique was making another fifty *soles* was neither here nor there. But Delphine had been specific about price and Vanessa knew that if she returned to England having paid more than her employer for the same kind of goods, it was not the most auspicious way of obtaining her longed-for partnership!

'I'll have to think it over,' she said politely. 'I have other women to visit and I'll come back and let you know what I decide to do.'

'The other women will not be any cheaper,' Maria stated. 'You will not do better.'

'What will happen if I decide your price is too high? Do you have anywhere else to sell your goods?'

'There is always the market and plenty of tourists.'

'Tourists don't come here all the year round,' said Vanessa, 'and if I'm prepared to buy from you on a regular basis—and to take everything you make—don't you think you would do better with me?'

Discomfiture was visible on the squat brown features as Maria looked at the children. They had finished their meagre meal and were playing quietly on the floor. 'I would sell if I could, but we have all promised . . .' She lowered her head and stared down at her work-worn hands.

Vanessa's eyes rested on them too. They were red and chapped, the fingers gnarled like an old tree and the nails broken from work. Pity stirred inside her. If only she could pay what the woman had asked! Anger towards Madame Delphine flared and died.

'I will think about it,' she repeated, and went out.

Two more visits to two other houses produced the same result as her meeting with Maria, and Vanessa, remembering what had happened in Cuzco and Pizoc, was convinced something—or someone—was making the women behave this way. Here was no haphazard decision to ask for more money but a deliberately planned operation. Nor could she believe that any of the women had master-minded it; they lacked the knowledge and none of them had sufficient authority to exercise their opinion over the others. No, the whole thing stemmed from one source and she had to find it. If she didn't, her entire journey to Peru would have been wasted.

Accepting the futility of seeing any more of the names on her list, she went to the main square, knowing that though it was not market day, she would always find Indians selling something. She was right. Spread out on the ground were mounds of dried meats, bundles of maize, barley and potatoes and heaped piles of blankets, predominantly striped in red and black. Trying to look like an innocent tourist and not the hard-hearted bargainer she was beginning to feel, she stopped in front of an old woman and enquired their price. She was met with a blank stare and she wrote down the amount and held out the paper. The old woman—were there no young ones here, or did they all age prematurely? Vanessa wondered—looked at the figure and shook her head. Vanessa hesitated, crossed out the numbers and increased the offer by ten per cent.

This was met by another shake of the head and she tried, by miming, to ask what price was wanted. Either the Indian did not understand or she was unwilling to answer, for she lowered her head on her chest until her face was hidden by her wide-brimmed, brown felt hat. With her squat body and bent legs she looked like an overdressed Buddha, but Vanessa was in no mood to laugh. The conspiracy to stop her from buying anything was beginning to have sinister overtones, and she was more conscious than ever of being miles away from anyone she knew.

With a casual nod, as if she did not mind being unable to buy anything, she swung round on her heel and walked away, turning so quickly that the man watching her with beady eyes had no chance to pretend he was doing otherwise. Her heart raced, but she ignored it. It was natural that she should be the object of curiosity; European tourists were still too recent an arrival here for her own visit to be disregarded. Yet there had been something intent in the man's stare . . .

She glanced over her shoulder. He was following her. She quickened her pace and knew, without looking round, that he had done the same. She reached the corner of the square and, stopping with a deliberate sharpness that gave him no time to draw back, swung round and faced him.

Seeing him at close range she realised he was not a full-blooded Indian, though he was too swarthy to be called a *mestizo*. He was wearing Western clothes and the array of ballpoint pens in his jacket pocket was somehow reassuring. At least he didn't look as if he were carrying a gun!

'You are following me,' she said in English. 'Why?'

He did not answer and she repeated her statement in halting Spanish. Still he said nothing, and her annoyance increased. 'Perhaps you can tell me what I have to do in order to buy something here—or isn't this a market for selling?'

Only then did he give the faintest of smiles, though it was more a crinkling of the eyes than the mouth. 'Everyone is anxious to sell, *señorita*,' he replied in a light voice, 'but perhaps your price is too low.'

'I'm offering the same price a friend of mine paid when she

was here a few months ago.' His lids flickered and she knew she had said something to interest him. She rummaged in her bag for her employer's photograph. 'Do you know her?'

Without looking at it, he shrugged. 'She is Englishwoman with shop.'

'And she wants to stock it with Peruvian clothes,' Vanessa added. 'That's why I am here. She's been ill and has sent me in her place.'

'Is better she come herself and talk to my master. He one who controls now.'

His master. Vanessa hoped her triumph did not show. So she had been right in assuming someone was responsible for the way the women were behaving!

'I am Madame Delphine's representative,' she said. 'And *I* can see your master.'

'He speaks only to the boss lady.'

'I'm the boss lady too,' Vanessa continued without any hesitation, knowing such a thing would never be if she returned to England empty-handed. 'I'm Madame Delphine's partner, so it's quite in order for your master to talk to *me*.'

The young man pulled his lips back against his teeth and considered her statement.

'If you pay four times more than last time, you not need meet my master. That is price he is willing do business with you.'

'Except that I don't happen to be willing to do business with *him*,' Vanessa said spiritedly. 'I came here to deal with the women who make the clothes—not some middleman who's cut himself in for a profit!'

She eyed the young man with disfavour, having rapidly come to the conclusion that he himself was the master. Perhaps he had told the women he could get them better prices if they gave him a commission. Annoyed with herself for not realising this before, she turned her back on him and set off for the hotel.

She had walked for several hundred yards before her temper had cooled sufficiently for her to be able to absorb what she was seeing, and she slowed her steps and paused to look at a small but beautiful Spanish-style church. With what fervour the Conquistadores had spread their gospel; burning those who would not believe and building church after church for those who did; until today there were as many churches in the towns of Peru as there were pubs in the towns of England!

Her afternoon was spent in the same fruitless manner as her morning, and each time she left one of the houses on her list she looked for a sight of the young man to whom she had spoken earlier. But there was no sign of him, and she knew that later in the evening she would have to put in a call to her employer and ask for permission to pay the increased prices.

'Such a thing would never have happened if I'd been well enough to go,' Delphine was certain to say, and such was Vanessa's low spirits that she was half inclined to think the same.

Perhaps she should have been more positive in her handling of the women? Should have shown anger instead of resignation. But it was too late to do anything about it now. She was faced with a situation and, because Delphine was so opinionated, had to seek advice and not deal with it herself.

After dinner and several cups of coffee, her spirits revived sufficiently for her to decide that not even Delphine's bull-dozing manner would have achieved success had she come here. Leaving the room, she went over to the reception desk to book her call to London.

She had almost reached the clerk when the young man of the morning approached her. In the electric light his skin looked swarthier and his large, irregular teeth noticeably whiter because of it.

'I have come to take you to Señor de la Rivas,' he said, stopping in front of her. 'He wish see you.'

So the man was working for someone after all. She could not remember Delphine mentioning anyone of that name and made a mental note to enquire about him at the desk.

'If you give me the address I'll come along in the morning,' she said.

'He wants see you now.'

'It's too late and too cold for me to go out tonight.'

'My master wish it.' The young man spoke flatly, as if it were a command not to be denied. 'You come, please.'

She almost refused, then decided it was unwise to antagon-ise this Señor de la Rivas, whoever he might be. Besides, it was important for her to find out how he had managed to make so many women, over so wide an area, do as he ordered.

'Please wait while I get my coat,' she said, and went slowly up the stairs hoping her leisurely pace would convince the *mestizo* that though he might regard Señor de la Rivas as his master, she herself did not.

CHAPTER THREE

ANTICIPATING a brisk walk across muddy thoroughfares and narrow, cobbled streets, Vanessa put on stout shoes and donned a heavy coat and head scarf. The desk clerk watched impassively as she went past him and she wished she had had the opportunity to ask him if he knew of Señor de la Rivas. It seemed foolhardy to set out at this time of night, in a strange country, to meet someone she did not know.

When she saw the huge Range Rover parked outside the hotel, with the young half-breed motioning her to get in, she almost turned tail and rushed back inside the lobby. Then common sense reasserted itself and she did as he had signalled, telling herself that anyone who owned a vehicle of such magnificence and newness could not be unknown in Puno.

'Have we far to go?' she asked as they drove off.

'An hour, perhaps.'

'An hour!' Her nervousness returned with full force. One could traverse the whole of the town and back in half that time. 'I thought Señor de la Rivas lived in Puno,' she said.

'He live in valley. It has good climate. He says like Mediterranean.'

Ignoring such hyperbole, Vanessa settled down to make the best of the journey, but, some forty minutes later when they were careering down a narrow winding road that seemed to be cut out of bare volcanic rock, she found it less of an exaggeration than she had supposed.

The air was distinctly warmer here despite the lateness of the hour, with a humidity that could almost be felt. The barren plain of the upper region had given way to a carpet of moss, and trees and shrubs were also making their appearance. The further they descended the more profuse the trees became, until soon a veritable forest lay on one side of her, while the other side of the valley was carved into narrow terraces, each one cultivated.

Lower and lower the Land Rover bumped, until at last they reached what she assumed was the bottom of the valley. At the same time the clouds scudded away from the moon and she saw a large, rectangular-shaped stone house, two storeys high. Ordinarily she would not have found its size intimidating, for it was little larger than those she had seen in the suburbs of Lima. But compared with the primitive homes of the Indians, it was a veritable mansion. For twenty yards in front of it the ground was meticulously tended: the tall grasses mowed flat, the tropical-looking trees and the shrubs uniformly trimmed. But this only served to increase the wild jungle atmosphere of the rest of the vegetation, and gave the house an unreal quality of calmness, as if it were a dream in the middle of a nightmare.

Nervously she pulled open her coat. No doubt her fanciful thoughts were caused by the heat: it must be seventy degrees at the least. She glanced at the young man beside her. He was manoeuvring the jeep to a stop, his eyes narrowed in concentration. When he had parked it to his satisfaction he jumped out and waited for her to do the same before leading the way to a heavy, nail-studded door.

It was made of a wood she did not recognise, but its dark colour went well with the grey stone walls. There were narrow slits for windows and she guessed there would be proper ones on the walls that faced into the inner patio. Her guide banged on the door and his hand was raised to knock on it again when it was swung back by an old Indian man with a wrinkled, nut-brown face. He wore white cotton trousers and a loose-fitting white shirt, both of which were surprisingly clean.

As if he were expecting them, he shuffled quickly ahead, and Vanessa only had a brief glimpse of a dimly lit hall—long and narrow and running on either side of her—before she was obliged to follow the old man down the right-hand corridor. Here too the walls were of stone, though the inner one was marked by doors, all of them hand-carved. Quickly she realised that all the rooms faced inwards. It was a style common to Spain and Middle East countries, but considering this house was set in a tropical wilderness, the desire for privacy seemed paranoid.

The servant shuffled to a stop and knocked on the door in front of him. He waited and must have heard a reply which was too faint to be audible to Vanessa, for he turned the heavy iron handle and stepped aside to let her go in.

The room, like the hallway, was dimly lit and what lighting there was was concentrated around the massive stone fireplace. A voice from somewhere in the distance, deep and speaking an Indian dialect, directed itself to the servant, who replied in the same tongue before closing the door behind him, leaving Vanessa alone with the man she had heard but not yet seen.

'I am Ramon de la Rivas,' the voice said, and this time spoke in English, surprising her by its rich timbre and an accent so faint that it merely added distinction to the words. 'I hope your journey to my home was not too unpleasant? I told Manuel to drive slowly, but one cannot always be sure he will obey instructions. Like most young men he enjoys the feel of a powerful car beneath him.'

There was the sound of steps and a tall figure emerged from the gloom to stand on a large, thick rug. It was patterned with a variety of geometric shapes and looked like an artist's vision of an ancient Inca city.

The man, whom she could now see more clearly, could have stepped straight from that city himself. Had he worn colourful robes and a gold headdress he could also have passed for its king. He was one of the tallest men she had seen in Peru, six foot three at least, with well-shaped bones and steely muscles encased in a darkly bronzed skin. It did not have the sallowness of the Indian—there was too much warmth in it for that—and she intuitively sensed that those parts of his body which did not see the daily sun would be considerably lighter than the rest. He was unsmiling, which made one aware of the perfect symmetry of his features. The mouth was a well-controlled curve below a long straight nose, while winging eyebrows marked obliquely set eyes. His cheekbones were sharp, the jawline clearly defined without being angular and the forehead high and looking more so by the way his hair sprang thickly up and away from it. It was a compelling face, with a haunting quality that reminded her of the Aztec mask of a warrior she had recently seen in the British Museum. But it was a hard face too, without a trace of gentleness. Here was a man born to command; born of ancestors who had commanded. It was as much a part of him as hardship was to the old Indian who had shown her into this room.

'Please sit down and let me offer you a drink,' he said. 'I am sure you are in need of one after your journey here.'

The voice was still as deep, but some undercurrent in it brought her back to the realisation that she was staring at him; which she might not have needed to do, she thought irritably, had there been more light in the room.

'What will you have?' he continued. 'There's some passable wine—I tend to keep my best vintages in Lima—or I can offer you spirits—whisky, gin, brandy?'

'Nothing, thank you.'

'Coffee, then?'

She accepted out of politeness rather than from a desire for any, and watched as he picked up a beautifully chased silver pot and poured fragrant black liquid into a white and gold cup that would not have disgraced a display cabinet in an English stately home. As he leaned forward to pass it to her, the light from a carved lamp-holder on the wall spilled on to his head, and she noticed with surprise that his hair was not the black she had supposed it to be, but rich brown. Curiosity about his ancestors stirred in her, but she resisted the urge to look at him as he handed her the cup, and instead kept her eyes fixed on the saucer.

'Sugar?' he asked.

'No, thank you.' She paused. 'May we discuss your reason for bringing me here?'

'Of course.'

He seated himself in a tall-backed chair a few yards away from her and crossed one long leg over the other. The light seemed brighter where he was sitting—or else her eyes had become accustomed to the gloom—for she could now make out that he was wearing tightly fitting trousers in charcoal grey with a paler grey silk shirt. Instead of a tie, a blue scarf was knotted carelessly at his throat, giving him the air of a man whose home was the Riviera or anywhere else that the jet set played. He moved slightly and this time the light illumined his face, making her quickly amend her last thought. Here was no man who played at anything; whatever he did was done in earnest, be it business or pleasure.

'I understand from the—er—from Manuel,' she said quickly, 'that if I want to buy any garments from the women in Puno, I must agree the price with *you*.'

'Not only in Puno,' he added, 'but also in any village in the Department of Puno.'

'Department?'

'In England I believe you would call it a county.'

Her mouth tightened. 'You have a large sphere of influence, *señor*.'

'I am an influential man.'

The softness of his tone gave the words more force, and she found it strange that a man of influence should concern himself with what she felt to be paltry matters. What possible difference did it make to him if the Indian women received a little more or a little less for the things they made? Whatever they earned was better than nothing and he would be a fool if he did not realise it. Yet he was no fool—of that she was sure —and she must watch her step with him.

'I'm surprised you don't use your influence to encourage the women to sell as much as they can, *señor*. I'm sure they need the money.'

'They need it desperately, Miss Wayne.'

She was curious to know how he knew her name, but would not give him the pleasure of asking.

'Then why are you discouraging them from selling to me?' she asked. 'I'm willing to buy everything they can make.'

'You are very kind.' There was no mistaking his sarcasm. 'Is it because you know how badly they need your money that you are grinding them into the ground?'

'I beg your pardon?'

'It is not *my* pardon you should beg, Miss Wayne, but theirs!' The softness had gone from his voice and it rang out sharply. 'They are the ones who break their backs to spin the yarn and make it into fabric; who wear out their hands sewing endless seams without the benefit of a machine and ruin their eyes by knitting in candlelight!'

'You talk as if I'm forcing them to do it,' she protested.

'Of course you're not,' he said sarcastically. 'If they're willing to offer their goods at give-away prices, how can *you* be blamed for wanting to take advantage of it?'

'I'm not taking advantage of anyone!'

'Aren't you?' He set his cup on the tray and leaned towards her. 'When an educated woman offers an illiterate peasant a pittance for a garment she knows she can sell for more than fifty times what she paid for it, wouldn't you call that taking an advantage?'

Dumbfounded, Vanessa stared at him.

'You are speechless,' he said matter-of-factly. 'But it is better than making further excuses. I was in England a month ago and saw your boutique in Mayfair. I sent in a friend of mine to enquire the price of a poncho which you had in the window, and it was immediately evident to me that my people were not charging enough.'

'All shops work on a large mark-up,' Vanessa said firmly, deciding this man was ignorant about trade and needed to be given an explanation. 'There's rent and rates to pay as well as staff. And one must also take into account that one doesn't sell everything one buys. Because of that, fashion boutiques mostly work on a mark-up of a hundred and fifty per cent. But that doesn't mean it's all profit. After their expenses have been met, one mightn't be left with more than a quarter of that. And of course if the weather goes awry—a mild winter or a cold summer—one can be left with so much unsold stock that it wipes out the entire profit.'

'I am conversant with the way a business is run.' The deep voice was mocking. 'However, it isn't *your* profit that concerns me.'

'I'm glad to hear it,' she said sarcastically.

'It's the profit the Indian women are making,' he went on, ignoring her interruption. 'Though I actually do consider it excessive to sell an article for twenty pounds when you bought it for one!'

'You're forgetting the cost of importing the goods,' she said angrily. 'Madame Delphine has been here twice before and the trips are getting more expensive, not less.'

'Prices are increasing everywhere—except in the pockets of the Indians If you do not agree to pay them a reasonable amount, you will have to leave empty-handed.'

'And leave the women empty in pocket?'

'I will personally see they do not lose by it.' He rose and went to stand by the fireplace, his height not dwarfed by its massive stone bulk.

'Are you also prepared to buy everything they make?' Vanessa asked. 'That's what *we're* willing to do.'

'So am I,' he said implacably. 'Until such time as I can make arrangements for them to sell their goods elsewhere.'

'To tourists in the market? You are forgetting one other thing, *señor*. Not only can we take everything the women make—we're willing to have them increase it!'

'And turn the Andes into a sweat-shop! *Madre mia!* Are you not ashamed of yourself!'

'How dare you talk to me like that?' Vanessa snapped, and jumped to her feet.

'I dare because I have the right!' he snapped back. 'Does knowing how much the women need your money give you the right to offer them the smallest possible amount? I'm well aware you've come a long way and have high costs in transport, but there's still too great a discrepancy between what you pay and the prices at which you sell. Your boutique is well known in London, Miss Wayne, and you should——'

'It isn't my boutique,' she intervened. 'I only work there.'

'You told Manuel you were Madame Delphine's partner.' The voice was cool. 'To pretend otherwise will make no difference to what I have said. If you want to return to the hotel and think it over . . .'

'I can't increase the price I offered without first talking to Madame Delphine.'

'When you see her, I am sure you will be able to convince her you were right to do as I ask. The prices you pay will still enable you to show an exorbitant profit.'

'How you hate the word profit,' Vanessa retorted. 'Are you angry because you aren't making one yourself? Is it because we aren't using you as our agent that you're trying to prevent us dealing direct with these women?'

The anger she had sensed in him earlier was nothing to the anger that was now visible. It glittered from his eyes and made a harsh line of his mouth.

'Do you think Ramon de la Rivas would take one centavo away from these poor wretches who can barely keep body and soul together? You would do well to know your facts, *señorita*, before you make such statements. If I did not know you were a stranger to my country, I would . . .'

She was never to know what he would have done, for he swung away from her as if he could no longer bear to look at her.

'There's no disgrace in being an agent,' she said clearly. 'It was not my intention to offend you, *señor*, but I can think of no other reason why you should concern yourself in my affairs.'

'Concern!' He swung round to face her. 'You use the word without knowing what it means. It is *entirely* my concern. I am concerned to guard the Indians against predators like yourself. I am concerned for their welfare; concerned to see they aren't exploited!'

'I'm not stealing what they make!' she cried. 'I'm willing to pay for it!'

'A pittance! That's what you're offering. Would *you* break your nails weaving wool for fifty pence a poncho? Or sit up through the night knitting sweaters when your bones ache from scrubbing floors and cooking meals and taking care of your family? If you knew the way these women worked, you wouldn't insult them by offering them such a price.'

'You're the one who's insulting,' she stormed. 'The women may regard you as their lord and master, but as far as I'm concerned you're an interfering tyrant!'

Surprise held him rigid; then he swallowed hard and spoke. 'Since you see me as a tyrant, then a tyrant I will be.' Eyes whose colour she had not yet distinguished glittered like coals from behind half-closed lids. 'You obviously lack the imagination to appreciate something you have not personally experienced, so I will put you in the same situation as the women you are trying to exploit.'

'I'm not trying to exploit *anyone*!' She was almost crying with temper. 'I refuse to discuss this with you any longer. Please ask your driver to take me back to my hotel.'

'Not yet. First you will weave the wool to make a poncho; then you will knit a cardigan and prepare the fur skin to make a jacket. Once that has been accomplished you will have a better understanding of what constitutes a fair price for the garments you wish to purchase.'

Vanessa gaped at him, unable to believe she had heard correctly, yet his expression told her he meant every word he had said.

'It is foolish of you to threaten me, *señor*.' She was glad her fear did not manifest itself in her voice, which remained remarkably calm. 'We have both lost our tempers and said things we didn't mean. I have promised you I will think over what——'

'Your idea of thinking it over will be to pack your bags and leave Peru as fast as you can!'

'Do you blame me?' she cried. 'Our boutique did well before we started selling Peruvian clothes and it will do equally well without them.' She went to side-step him, but he reached out and savagely clamped his hand on her arm.

'Where will you go next?' he demanded. 'Bolivia? Chile? Ecuador? There are plenty of impoverished nations in the world waiting for you to come and cheat them!'

'Let go of me!' She tried to pull away from his hold. 'You give yourself the airs of an aristocrat, but you've got the manners of a savage! Let go of my arm and ask your man to drive me back to my hotel.'

'No.'

He relinquished his hold on her but remained so close that she had to tilt her head back to look into his face. What she saw there was not reassuring. His eyes were narrow slits and his mouth was curled into a smile that was merely a twist of the lips and disclosed sharp white teeth.

'I have already explained to you, Miss Wayne, that you will remain here until you have completed three tasks. Not until then will you be free to leave and, I hope, willing to offer a reasonable price to all the women who are so anxious to work for you.'

Despairingly she shook her head. 'Even if I wanted to pay the price you ask, I couldn't do so without Madame Delphine's authority. I'm not her partner, *señor*. If you don't believe me, telephone her and speak to her yourself.'

His head inclined to one side, showing the smooth plane of his cheek and the side of his jaw. It looked as if it were carved from rock, and Vanessa shivered but clung to her control.

'I can give you the number of the nursing home where Madame Delphine can be contacted,' she continued. 'She is recovering from an operation—that's why she sent me here in her place—and she will confirm that she employs me and that I'm *not* her partner.'

Still he remained motionless and silent, and she opened her bag and scribbled down the telephone number of the nursing home as well as the boutique.

'P-please, *señor*,' she said shakily, holding out a piece of paper. 'Find out for yourself.'

He took the paper from her, regarded it for an instant and then nodded. 'It may take some time, Miss Wayne. I will have to call Lima and ask someone there to do it for me. To contact London from here is difficult.' He saw her expression and said, 'I have no telephone at the *hacienda*; only a radio transmitter and receiver.'

'I see.'

She tried to sound friendly, as if she already knew what the outcome of his call would be: apology on his side; acceptance of it on hers and probably some agreement on the prices she would have to pay for the clothes. Delphine was too shrewd not to give in.

'Please help yourself to more coffee,' he said. 'I will be as quick as I can.'

The door closed behind him and Vanessa sank down in the nearest chair, then jumped up again, too nervous to relax. What would happen if the man could not contact the nursing home or if Madame Delphine refused to take the call? But her employer would never do that. She would realise instantly that something was wrong. Hands clasped in agitation, Vanessa paced the room. It was dark beyond the small pool of light cast by the wall lamp, and she found the shadows so menacing that she returned to her chair.

As she did so, the door opened and the man came in.

'Did you get through?' she asked breathlessly.

'Yes.'

'Thank goodness!' Relief made her want to cry. 'Well, now you know I——'

'Madame Delphine wasn't there,' he cut in.

'Not there?' Vanessa ignored her rising fear. 'But she had an operation two weeks ago and——'

'She has gone away to convalesce. The nursing home did not have her address.'

'*Someone* must know. Did you call the boutique?' She frowned as she remembered the time difference. 'It must be dawn in London. But if you could call at nine-thirty in the morning, Greenwich time, Mrs Rogers—she works there with me—will confirm exactly what I've told you.'

'The boutique is closed.'

'But in the morning——'

'It is closed until the twenty-fifth of the month.' The man's voice was as cold as the wind that blew over the sierra. 'As you very well know,' he added.

'How could I have known? Anyway, you must have misunderstood what was said. It can't be closed.'

'It is. My secretary in Lima is highly efficient and *she* made the calls. She spoke to an answering service and they told her it is closed for repairs. A water main exploded and part of the premises were flooded.'

Vanessa was lost for words. Indeed the picture was so clear it did not require any. The temporary closing of the boutique was understandable in the circumstances, as was her employer's convalescence.

'Someone should know where Madame Delphine is,' she said. 'Either her doctor or her maid. I can give you the number of her apartment and——'

'My secretary obtained it from the nursing home. But that too is switched over to the answering service.'

'Can't *they* contact her?'

'Your partner is on a cruise and cannot be called. As you well know,' he repeated.

'I didn't,' she protested. 'Nor did I know the boutique was flooded. Why should I want to waste your time and antagonise you by having you make fruitless telephone calls? Please, *señor*, be reasonable!'

'My reason tells me you are a clever young woman who hoped the transatlantic calls would cool my temper and decide me to let you go. But you were not quite clever enough. All it has done is to confirm me in my decision.'

'You can't mean to keep me here. The joke has gone far enough, *señor*. Please let me leave.'

'For the moment your home is here.'

Angrily she marched to the door. It was heavy to open and she struggled with the handle, glancing nervously over her shoulder to see if he was coming after her. But he had resumed his occupation of the high-backed chair and was watching her with a mocking smile.

'Run as fast as you like, Miss Wayne. The road is steep and long and you would die of cold and hunger before you were even a quarter of the way back to Puno.'

Remembering the long drive across the *alto-plano* and the steep descent into the valley, she knew he was speaking the truth. To escape on foot was impossible. Without a car she was as much a prisoner here as if she were locked in a dungeon and chained in irons.

'If I'm not back at the hotel by the morning, *señor*, the clerk will report it to the police.'

'Manuel will return to the hotel and collect your luggage.' The deep voice came back at her across the room. 'He will settle your bill and explain that you are staying here as my guest.'

'What happens when you finally let me go?' she asked. 'Do you think I'll forget what happened? I'll report you to the police in Lima. I'll go and see the British Consul. By the time I've finished, your name will be ruined!'

'So will yours,' the man said softly. 'Even in today's permissive society, the woman suffers most by such scandal.'

'What scandal?'

Wide shoulders lifted in a shrug. 'Whatever you accuse me of, all I need say in my defence is that you were here as my *amorata*.' He paused and let his eyes move slowly along her body and then up to her face. 'Do I need to explain any more? It is not inconceivable that after some time in your company I could have required a change and suggested we part. In such circumstances women have been known to become— shall we say—difficult? There is a proverb to that effect, I believe; something about Hell having no fury like a——'

'You swine!' The words were wrenched from her and she lunged forward as if to hit him. Impassively he remained seated, not by a movement of his muscles showing any awareness of her action.

'I would be a bigger swine if I did not fight for my people,' he stated. 'Now I suggest you let me show you to your room. You are too overwrought for us to continue our discussion.'

Taking it for granted that she would follow him, he led the

way along the corridor. He walked with long, loping strides and Vanessa had to run to keep up with him. At the timbered front door he veered right towards the staircase. She had not seen it when she had entered the house, but now another oil lamp had been lit and its mellow gold light illumined the dark wood banisters and heavily carved rail.

Swiftly he climbed to the first floor. Here again all the rooms lay off a long corridor, though this one was used as a picture gallery, with sombre portraits lining the walls. She had no chance to look at them but guessed them to be the man's ancestors. He was still striding rapidly ahead of her and did not stop until he reached the last door and opened it.

Nervously she preceded him into a large bedroom, her panic subsiding a little as she took in her surroundings. Three oil lamps gave the room more than enough light for her to appreciate the sombre magnificence of the ornately carved dressing-table and fourposter bed. But it was the rest of the furnishings which caused her fear to lessen, for the curtains at the long windows were of filmy white silk trimmed with plaited pink cord, as was the coverlet on the bed and the two small easy chairs. The effect was feminine, though incongruous against the overpowering furniture and the overpowering man who owned it, and she was sure that a woman —and a young one at that—had been responsible for the decor.

She went to stand by the window. The frame was of the same unusual wood as the front door, and the panes of glass were thick and small. Her fingers were on the latch when he spoke.

'I wouldn't open it if I were you.'

'I won't try to escape,' she said icily. 'I have no desire to break my legs.'

'Nor to have insects fly in and feast themselves upon your soft white skin.'

She recoiled from him; partly at the image of insects devouring her, and partly at the silkiness of his voice as he had referred to her skin: almost as if he longed to devour it himself.

'If you find it too warm,' he went on prosaically, 'turn on the air-conditioning.' One lean brown finger indicated a switch on the wall near the bed.

'Air-conditioning?' she exclaimed in surprise. 'But you have no electricity.'

'We have an electric dynamo,' he corrected, and seeing her eyes move to the oil lamps, added: 'When I am alone I prefer these. It makes me feel closer to my ancestors.'

'Who were probably primitive savages,' she thought mutinously but silently, and turned hurriedly away from him.

'I won't let you keep me here.' Her voice shook with an anger she could no longer control and it brought tears to her eyes. 'I'll give in to you tonight because it's too dark and too late for me to do anything else. But in the morning I'm going back to Puno if I have to crawl there on my knees!'

'That's exactly what you'd have to do,' he said, and abruptly left her.

She stared at the closed door, then gripped her hands together and tried not to scream. She was a prisoner in the house of a madman—well, if not exactly mad, autocratic to the point of mania. A sharp rap on the door almost made her jump out of her skin as the man she had been thinking of appeared on the threshold.

'Manuel will go to the hotel in the morning to collect your clothes. Meanwhile one of the servants will bring you some night things.' He turned to go again and she called his name.

'Señor de la Rivas! I beg you to let me go. I'm willing to forget everything that's happened here. I won't tell anyone about it and I'll take the responsibility of paying the Indian women the prices you want.'

He looked at her levelly for what seemed a long time, yet could only have been a few seconds.

'My decision has been made, señorita, and I will not allow a woman's pleading to make me change it.'

For the second time the door closed behind him and Vanessa hit her hand against the side of the bed in impotent rage. There was nothing she could do and she knew it. What was worse—he knew it too. She was well and truly this man's prisoner.

CHAPTER FOUR

THE clinking of curtain rails being drawn over long brass poles awakened Vanessa and she sat up and saw a dour-faced Indian at the window. A black cotton skirt and blouse did nothing to relieve her lugubrious features, though the eyes—small and beady—did not look unfriendly as she murmured something incomprehensible and pointed at the small tray she had placed on the table beside the bed.

Vanessa looked at the beautifully worked silver coffee pot and jug; the latter was filled with strange-smelling milk which she took to be goat's milk, and there was a white porcelain plate filled with sugary-coated biscuits.

'Do you speak Spanish?' she asked, enunciating the words clearly, and the woman nodded and answered that if the *señorita* wished, she could breakfast in her room or downstairs in the patio.

'I'll come down,' said Vanessa, anxious to get the lie of the land and discover if there was any way of escape from this ridiculous situation.

The servant shuffled out and Vanessa sipped her coffee. It was far too strong, even with all the milk added, and she left it and went to shower. The bathroom was small but luxurious, the water hot, and there was delicious-smelling French soap and large, fluffy towels.

Since she had no change of clothes with her she was forced to wear the ones she had taken off last night. They were uncomfortably warm for this tropical climate and she undid a couple of buttons on her bodice and rolled back her sleeves. She did not have a comb for her hair and raked her fingers through it, glad it had a natural wave which, at this moment, gave it a voluptuous quality of untidiness. The sight of herself in the mirror enraged her and she marched determinedly downstairs.

In daylight she saw that only the outer walls were of stone, and that all the inner ones were rough-plastered, with black iron wall lights placed intermittently along them. The floor was stone, but so lustrous that it glowed like a silvery grey jewel, though it was not slippery underfoot. Moving further along the hall, Vanessa searched for a door to take her into the inner courtyard. She found one almost directly facing the front door, and she opened it gingerly and found herself in a patio more reminiscent of Spain than a valley deep in the heart of the Andes.

On a mosaic-tiled floor, its colours predominantly blue and white, stood several white wrought iron tables and chairs. The seats were softened by blue and white cushions and identical cushions lay on the white wood sun-loungers that hugged the shade of the far wall. Also taking advantage of the shade was a large golden labrador and, about to head for one of the tables which she saw laid for breakfast, Vanessa stood rigid as the dog rose and padded towards her. The sight of the wagging tail reassured her and she leaned down and held out her hand, palm forward, for the dog to sniff. Only when it had done so and given one of her fingers an encouraging lick did she pat its head.

'What a beauty you are,' she said softly. 'And far more friendly than your owner.'

'Who is more likely to have bitten your hand than to have licked it!' said a crisp voice, and Vanessa straightened swiftly to see her jailor in front of her.

In the sunshine he looked less like a black demon and more like a golden-brown Viking, with his bronze skin and rich brown hair curling crisply above his austerely planed face. Well-fitting jodhpurs were let into high, black leather boots, and a matching black belt clasped his waist. A silk shirt did little to disguise the fact there was bare skin beneath it and the half-buttoned front disclosed a thick tangle of dark hair on his chest, which almost hid the gold chain and medallion he wore. It glittered like an eye as he moved and she looked quickly away from it.

'Last night I thought you were older,' he said abruptly.

Surprise brought her eyes up to his and she saw they were narrowed as he frowned down at her.

'Does that mean you'll let me go?' she asked.

'No.'

He gave an arrogant turn of his head. There was something familiar about the movement and memory stirred in her.

Where had she seen that disdainful gesture before? Suddenly she remembered. It had been at the restaurant where Don had taken her. This man had come in with a party of people and she had been struck by his height and lordly manner. What a good judge of character she had been!

'Have you had breakfast, Miss Wayne?'

His question interrupted her thoughts and she was glad he had not been able to read them.

'No, *señor*, I haven't.'

'Then I will have someone attend to you.'

He strode towards a door, stopping as an old woman emerged from it wheeling a trolley. A thermos of coffee and several silver tureen dishes reposed on the top shelf, with brightly coloured crockery and matching table linen on the one below. With humour tinged with irritation, Vanessa watched as a table was laid. Though he lived in the wilds, Señor de la Rivas made sure it was a life of elegance.

The servant set out the last plate and bobbed in the direction of the man, the submissive sign at variance with her sullen expression. He nodded back and said something in a tongue Vanessa did not comprehend. It was evidently a joke, for the woman gave a toothless grin and cackled. Autocratic or not, her jailor was evidently liked by his servants.

'Please have your breakfast,' he said to Vanessa, and straddled a chair by the table to watch her.

Not sure whether he knew she found his presence unnerving—and was remaining with her deliberately—she did her best to ignore him and helped herself to a maize cake and some highly spiced sausages.

'We can provide fruit and toast if you prefer it?' he ventured, seeing her make a face as she bit into the first piece of meat.

'No, thank you, *señor*.' Her eyes were cold. 'I thought prisoners only had bread and water?'

He did not rise to her baiting and she poured herself some coffee and sipped it. It was still too strong and she set down the cup with a barely suppressed shudder.

'Is it not good?' he asked.

'I find it rather strong for my taste.'

'I'm not doing very well as a host, am I?' he said dryly,

and snapped his fingers in the direction of the door nearest to him.

A young boy appeared as if by magic and Vanessa guessed he had been peering at them through one of the narrow slits in the stone. There was an exchange of dialogue and the lad ran off with the thermos flask.

'He will bring you a weaker brew,' the man said. 'The servants are used to making it for me, and I like it strong and bitter.'

'Naturally.'

One silky eyebrow rose. 'I am sorry you see *me* that way too, *señorita*. But when I defend the rights of a downtrodden race, I am inclined to be ruthless.'

'Paying a higher price for the things they make won't help them very much. It will take more than a few individuals and a dress shop to change their life!'

'I'm well aware of that,' he said bitterly. 'I've spent half my own life trying to get the authorities to take action. The Indians number half our population and the burden of caring for them falls on a small minority.'

'What you mean,' she corrected coldly, 'is that the wealth of your country is owned by ten per cent of its people.'

'The guide books you have been reading are out of date, Miss Wayne. Since the last few years the Government has redistributed a great part of that wealth. Our main industries have been nationalised, land reform is well under way and education is compulsory for everyone until they are fourteen. We still have enormous difficulties to overcome, of course, and we're hampered by the harsh terrain as well as the weather. Many parts of our country are inaccessible in the rainy season. Added to that, there are still a vast number of Indians who do not want to be assimilated into the political or economic life of Peru and remain a great drain on its resources.'

'Maybe they're scared of assimilating.'

'They must be taught otherwise.'

'Will keeping me a prisoner help them to develop?' she asked sweetly.

'Even if you paid a thousand times more, it would still only be a drop in the ocean.'

'Then why——'

'One must make a start somewhere.'

He fell silent as the boy returned with the coffee. This time it was more to her taste and she sipped it with a pleasure she was careful to hide.

'Manuel should soon be back with your clothes,' the man continued. 'He will also arrange for the hotel to call us if there are any messages for you.'

'Then you do have a telephone!'

'Only a receiver and a transmitter—as I told you last night. We live primitively here, señorita.'

She thought of the piping hot water in the bathroom; her luxuriously appointed bedroom with its air-conditioning, and the silver dishes on the table in front of her.

'Very primitively,' she said dryly. 'I could almost mistake your home for an Indian one!'

His indrawn breath was his only sign of anger, and since she had meant to annoy him, she stared at him defiantly. There was no mercy in the thin line of his mouth nor compassion in his eyes. She noticed that in the sunlight they were as rich a brown as his hair, and she had the impression there were gold flecks in them. But his lids lowered to mask them before she could be sure.

'Do not try my patience too far, señorita, or I might put you to live with an Indian family. Then you would really appreciate the hardship they suffer.'

'Since you feel so strongly for them I'm surprised you haven't turned your home into a commune!'

'They would not enjoy living as my equal. Their Inca heritage has given them the need to have a master whom they can obey.'

'You?'

'In this region only. But have no fear for them. I do not beat them nor use them as slave labour—hard though you may find this to believe!'

With a lithe movement he stepped back from the chair, and the dog—who had been lying patiently at his feet—rose too.

'When Manuel returns with your clothes I suggest you change into something cooler. Then I will show you the work I have arranged for you to do.'

Vanessa bit back a sharp retort, refusing to give him the satisfaction of knowing how angry she was; and how impot-

ent she felt. It was this latter feeling which was the most difficult to bear. No man had ever been her master, yet here was
this foreign savage telling her what to do. Worse than that—
commanding her. It was an experience she vowed to revenge,
come what may.

Soon after returning to her room, Manuel arrived with her
case. It looked small in the large bedroom and for the first
time she wondered how long Señor de la Rivas intended to
keep her here. She only had enough clothes for a short trip
and none of them were suitable for this heat.

Even when she had put on her coolest dress she still found
it too heavy, and was again forced to leave the bodice partly
undone and the sleeves pushed back. Her hair was damp with
perspiration and she pinned it away from her face as best she
could, wishing she had bought some of the beautifully worked
silver combs so profusely displayed in the markets. She must
remember to do so before she left Peru.

If she ever did leave Peru.

The thought was disquieting and she tried not to think of
it as she returned to the downstairs hall. Señor de la Rivas was
waiting for her, his face expressionless as he asked her to follow him. She had no intention of asking where they were
going, but her curiosity grew as they left the house and
headed for the Land Rover. It was a modern and reassuring
sight amidst this jungle of greenery, and she marvelled that it
had travelled the tortuous road that snaked down the side of
the steep valley.

In daylight, the walls of the valley were more spectacular
than she had imagined. Some five thousand feet high, their
sides were a wall of vegetation that became thicker and more
luxuriant the lower it descended. A garden of Eden in a barren wilderness; there was no other way to describe it.

The eastern slopes were carved into narrow terraces and
were intensively cultivated, forming strips of variegated
greens and browns, dependent on what was being grown on
them. But the bottom of the valley could have been part of
the Amazon jungle, for it bore no resemblance to the barren
terrain of the *alto-plano* some five thousand feet above it.
Here grew avocados, oranges, papayas and other tropical
fruits Vanessa did not recognise; while colourful birds flitted
from branch to branch and settled along the banks of the nar-

row but swift-flowing river that coursed along the valley floor like a jugular vein.

The *hacienda* was built on a wide plateau several hundred feet above the rushing water, and she assumed that this was because it was less humid here and received more light and air Despite this, it was very hot, and as she took her seat in the car she was thankful for the cover of the roof. The engine came throatily alive and she wondered how far she was from Puno. Not many miles if she travelled in a straight line, but a long distance if she took into account the steep vertical climb.

Señor de la Rivas took the wheel and she was disconcerted to find she was going to be alone with him. She had assumed Manuel would be driving this heavy vehicle and she watched surreptitiously as narrow, tanned hands firmly shifted gear. The jeep swung round and she was given her first daylight glimpse of his house.

It was considerably larger than it had appeared last night, though its stone walls, steeply pitched roof and narrow slits for windows gave no sign of the luxury within. Maybe it was as well that the poverty-stricken Indians did not know in what comfort their master lived. They might not be so happy to work for him if they saw what their sweated labour had given him!

Even as she thought this, she knew it was untrue. The servants who worked at the *hacienda* knew every detail of the way the house was run and no doubt imparted their knowledge to all their family and friends. She remembered Señor de la Rivas saying the Indians needed to depend on someone, and could well imagine them looking upon him as a god. If only she could find a way of bringing him down from his self-imposed pedestal! Fury engulfed her and it was all she could do not to hit out at him, either physically or with her tongue.

The jolting of the vehicle brought her sharply back to an awareness of her surroundings, and she clung to the side as they started the laborious climb upwards. The man beside her did not speak, his attention fully given to the narrow twisting road. But after a while it became less tortuous and he changed gear and pointed a finger past her and downwards.

'If you look below you will get an excellent view of the valley,' he said.

She peered out. From this height she was looking into a steep crevasse of green, broken only by the river, which interlaced it like a narrow ribbon of silver.

'There are many valleys like this,' he went on. 'Though none perhaps quite so fertile. We provide much of the food in the area; without it there would be starvation.'

'Why don't all the Indians live down here?' she asked. 'It's a better climate than the plains.'

'They prefer to live as their ancestors have done. The only ones you find in the valleys are those whose families have always lived down here.'

He paused, and she refrained from asking the many questions on her lips. She was not going to give him the satisfaction of making conversation with him.

'My own family have been here for many generations,' he continued, as if piqued by her lack of curiosity. 'They settled eventually in Lima but still kept this *hacienda*. It was here they first put down their roots.'

'A remote place in which to do so,' she commented.

'The first de la Rivas actually settled in Cuzco. Then he chanced upon this valley and built the house. He used it as his base while he searched for Inca gold.'

'One of Pizarro's band of cut-throats?' she asked.

'I see you know something of my country's history.'

'I know it was pillaged by the Spaniards. I'm not surprised you wish to make amends today, *señor*.'

'And that I don't wish to see *you* pillage the poor Indians?'

She was annoyed for making a trap for herself, but he did not press home his victory and instead concentrated on the road, which had become steeper again.

'I assume you had all your necessary shots before leaving England?' he asked suddenly.

'All the regulation ones,' she replied, and felt a tremor of fear. 'Are there others I should have had before coming to this part of the country?'

'No. But you should peel your fruit and never drink water unless it's been boiled. One easily gets fever here, and if you sweat a lot you must also remember to take salt tablets—I'll get you some when we return home. You should also change your clothes when they get damp.'

'I didn't come equipped for that,' she said coldly.

'I thought your case was rather small,' he admitted. 'I was surprised a beautiful young woman in the couture business should travel so light.'

'I only brought bare necessities with me. I thought it was important for me to be able to carry my own case if necessary.'

'Intelligent as well as beautiful.'

She let the remark pass and they drove on in silence.

'You are a seasoned traveller?' he asked finally.

'No, señor. This is the first time I've been on a buying trip.'

'Indeed?'

His tone was so disbelieving that she was impelled to answer him.

'My *employer* does the buying. She's never even let me go to the Continent.'

'Yet she sent you to Peru?' His tone was silky.

'Because she was ill and couldn't come here herself.'

'That is what you told me last night. But it isn't what you said to Manuel when you spoke to him in the market yesterday morning.'

'I saw no point in going into details with him,' she snapped. 'At that time I didn't know I was going to be taken prisoner.' Her sense of frustration was so great that she swung round on him, forgetting her vow not to show her anger. 'I can't force you to believe me, but even if you keep me here for ever, I'll never be able to pay the Indians what you're demanding. Only Madame Delphine can authorise me to do that.'

'You know very well I can't reach her.'

'Then wait until she returns to the boutique. Or wait until it opens. When you talk to Mrs Rogers she'll confirm everything I've told you.'

'You will still do the tasks I have set for you,' he stated. 'Even if your story is true, it will at least help you to make your'—his hesitation was deliberate—'your employer appreciate the effort that goes into the making of each garment.'

Knowing it was fruitless to continue the discussion—no matter what she said he would only believe what he wanted—Vanessa turned her back on him and looked at the scenery. The valley had widened considerably and she no longer had a feeling of being hemmed in by it. Above her was the blue sky that always held more than a hint of cloud, and on the furthest, uppermost slopes which closely bordered the flat plains, the land was already looking sparse.

'Are we leaving the valley?' she asked.

'No.'

As he spoke they came to a fork in the narrow road and he took the one which descended again, and which brought them almost down to the river and a flat area of land on which stood a huddle of stone huts with thatched roofs. Was this the Indian homestead where she would be working? Her lips compressed as they increased speed for the last few hundred yards and bumped their way over the grassy land to the settlement.

At close hand she saw there were several dozen dwellings and an assortment of large sheds, and she wondered if this was where the estate workers lived. If so, the *hacienda* was a vast one.

The man beside her jumped down from the Land Rover and came round the side to help her alight. Ignoring his hand, she climbed down unaided. He gave no sign of noticing her refusal to accept his help and strode ahead of her to the nearest shed, stopping by the entrance until she had caught up with him.

'I suppose you do know what happens to sheep wool once it's been sheared?' he asked coldly.

The question was so unexpected that she almost smiled. But she caught herself in time.

'I once saw a film about it,' she said casually. 'Is that what *I'm* supposed to do—wash the wool and sort it?'

'No. The women here leave that to the men—and so can you. But I want you to see what happens to the llama's wool once it's been sheared.'

'Llamas?' she queried.

'We find them better than sheep for our purposes.' Pushing open the door, he motioned her to precede him.

For the next hour Vanessa could almost believe she had been transported into another world in another century. Not a century of the future either, but one where machines had not yet taken over the effort of heavy manual work, and where human beings laboured like animals.

First she was shown great bundles of fleece, mainly grey in colour but some of it black or fawn. Each bundle was undone and shaken loose so that it could then be heated until the fibres swelled and the wool had become sufficiently soft for it to be teased apart. Once this was done it was spread out over wire netting and the dust and dirt picked out by hand—a tedious and filthy job that could not be hurried. Then the different qualities of fleece were separated, and though to Vanessa's inexperienced eye each mound looked identical, the Indians had no difficulty in dividing them into different piles, according to colour and quality.

'The next step is to cure the wool,' Señor de la Rivas said, leading her from one large shed to another. 'It is not pleasant to watch, but I wish you to see everything.'

Tilting her head higher, she stalked after him, pride refusing to let her admit she was finding the whole exercise a fascinating one.

During her training at fashion college she had seen this particular process done in a mill in the Midlands, where everything had been automated, and it bore no resemblance to the scene she was watching now. It was like being in the ante-room of Dante's Inferno. Huge deep vats of scouring liquid bubbled and boiled, and the steam-laden air was malodorous with benzine. Dour-faced men vigorously stirred the vats with long-pronged forks, continually moving the sodden mass of fleece until Vanessa wondered—head swimming with fumes—whether it would melt away into nothing. She turned to look into another vat and the shed swung around her alarmingly. She put out a hand to try and steady herself and found it gripped by a hard one.

'I told you it wasn't pleasant,' a grim voice said, and she found herself half pulled, half carried out into the reviving air.

A few lungfuls of it and she was back to normal and able to look at her captor with venom. 'You won't achieve anything by showing me this,' she snapped. 'All it does is prove to me how shortsighted your government is. If they spent less money building dams on the coast and more money teaching the Indians modern methods of agriculture and manufacturing, you wouldn't need to rely on a boutique in London to keep them from starvation!'

'I agree with you.'

'You do?' His capitulation caught her unawares and she

was not sure what to say. But before she could gather her wits, he was speaking again.

'However, I cannot take on the whole Government, much as I would like to, so I must take on those I can—*you* and others like you—until such time as the rest of the world accepts responsibility for what is happening here.'

'Why should the rest of the world be responsible for Peru?'

'Because *their* greed is affecting our economy. Because the money they pour into our country is only used to further their own wants. Do you know that Peruvian fishermen catch more fish in a month than Britain does in a year? And that it's nearly all made into pig's food and shipped to the Western world, while one in five of our own children dies from starvation?'

Helplessly she stared at him, able to appreciate his frustration and liking him far more than she had done at any time since they met. But she had to make him see how pointless it was for him to wreak his anger upon herself.

'I can understand how you feel, *señor*, but I still can't see how keeping me here will help your countrymen.'

'One must do what one can,' he said harshly, and pointed to a large stack of white and black fibre bundles which were being put into a reed basket and carried over to the jeep. 'I take it you don't know how to spin?'

'Nor will I,' she exclaimed.

'I have arranged for one of the women to come to the *hacienda* and teach you,' he answered, ignoring her outburst.

'You're wasting your time.'

'It's *your* time that's being wasted, Miss Wayne. The quicker you do as I ask, the quicker you'll be able to leave here.'

Mutinously Vanessa ran to the jeep. It was only a few yards away, but her skin was wet by the time she reached it. She rubbed her hand across her face. Her hair was soaking and rivulets of moisture ran down her forehead. If she didn't find something cooler to wear she would die of heat-stroke before that bully behind her could teach her anything!

He reached her side, but did not speak as he swung the vehicle round and headed back the way they had come. The higher they climbed the cooler it became, though it was still excessively warm when they reached the plateau where the *hacienda* had been built. Vanessa only had one cotton dress into which she could change and as soon as the Land Rover came to a halt, she jumped out and headed for the house.

'Don't disappear, *señorita*, you have work to do!'

'I want to put on something cooler. I won't be any good to you if I pass out from the heat.'

Even white teeth nibbled at his lower lip. 'Very well. I will see you in the library.'

'Do I have to clock in and clock out?' she demanded.

'Once you have been shown what to do, you can work at your own speed. But the longer it takes you to finish the three garments you must make, the longer you will stay here.'

'Then I'll work till I drop!'

'I'm sorry you don't like my home.'

'It's fine for barbarians!' she flashed, and raced up the stairs. She knew her comment was unjustified, but she did not care. She hated Ramon de la Rivas more than she had hated anyone in her life.

CHAPTER FIVE

VANESSA took her time changing and it was more than an hour before she went downstairs. Her cotton dress was cool against her skin and she knew she would have to wash and iron it every day; it was impossible for her to wear any of her warmer clothes here.

Following Señor de la Rivas' instruction, she went to the room where she had met him the previous night. It was empty and she assumed he had grown tired of waiting for her.

She hung around for a while, passing the time by looking at the books that lined the whole of one wall. They were mostly in Spanish, but there was a varied selection in English and French, mostly dealing with politics and economics. If these were his, then his taste was surprisingly catholic. From the little she knew of him, she had judged him to be rigid in his ideas, and wondered if, like so many people today, he had double standards: everyone around him had to do the right and moral thing, but he could live the way he liked. She stopped short. Why should she think of him in derogatory terms? Harsh he might be, but surely no lover of the flesh-pots would choose to live in this solitary place, well furnished and comfortable though it was? And there was undoubtedly something sensuous about him, as evidenced by the way he walked and the magnetism he exuded.

Nervous at where her thoughts were taking her—for she must be the only white woman for hundreds of miles—Vanessa wandered into the courtyard.

The clouds had lifted and it was no longer oppressive. She sank on to a chair and rubbed her hand along one of its arms, wishing for a cool drink. As if the arm of the chair was a genie's lamp, the old crone who had served her breakfast came towards her carrying a silver-topped glass pitcher filled with golden liquid and two crystal glasses. She set them on the table and Vanessa smiled her thanks and poured herself a drink. It was orange juice laced with something she couldn't define, and she was still sipping it when firm steps sounded behind her. She refused to turn and even when a dark shadow lay across her feet, she gave no sign of seeing it.

'I asked you to meet me in the library,' Ramon de la Rivas said.

'You weren't there.'

'I grew tired of waiting for you and went to do some other things. Please come with me.'

His tone warned her not to ask for time to finish her drink and she set it down and followed him into the house. He did not take her to the library but to a rectangular room at the other end of the corridor. The walls were unplastered but shone with the patina of continual polishing, as did the tiled floor. In the corner of the room stood a spinning wheel. It was extremely old but beautifully kept, and Vanessa moved closer to look at it. Something told her it had come from Spain; possibly brought by the wife of the first de la Rivas to settle here.

'The women of our family have used it for years,' the man behind her said, his words proving her right. 'My mother was expert at spinning.'

'You can't be serious about wanting *me* to do it?' she exclaimed, swinging round.

'I am perfectly serious.'

He looked past her, his expression softening, and she saw that a squat Indian woman had come in. She had the usual impassive face of her race, but when she spoke her voice was full of animation.

Vanessa could not follow what was said, but after a brief exchange, the man went to the door.

'Josefina will show you what to do. You might find it difficult to begin with, but the quicker you put your heart into the task, the easier it will become.'

He went out and Vanessa swallowed her anger and regarded the woman. Josefina, if that was her real name, was here on her master's bidding, and could not be blamed for what she had to do. If only she spoke English and could help her to escape!

'Do you live in the *hacienda*?' she asked in carefully enunciated Spanish.

The woman stared at her blankly and with a sigh Vanessa realised Josefina only spoke her own language. No wonder the Peruvian Government had made it compulsory for everyone at school to learn Spanish! It was impossible to integrate a country when one half of the population could not communicate with the other!

Yet though she and Josefina had no common language, the woman was an excellent teacher. Her wrinkled old hands, with their short broken nails, had the delicacy of a surgeon's touch as they manipulated the fleece into threads. Long fibres were attached to a distaff of wood and held under her left arm, while the short fibres were on a carded roll held in her hand. The spindle itself was about fifteen inches long and she attached a long fibre to it and began to twirl, pulling out the wool to form one continuous strand. The yarn produced had a fineness and delicacy that could not have been excelled by any modern machine, and Vanessa watched until the wheel stopped turning and she was beckoned to take the stool Josefina was vacating.

She shook her head, knowing she could never copy the old woman, but strong hands pushed her on to the seat and showed her how to begin. Vanessa tried to repeat the action, but the thread broke, and though she kept on trying, at no time could she spin a length longer than half a metre.

'It's impossible!' she cried finally, and jumped up in exasperation, sending the chair crashing behind her.

Josefina's face creased into a wide smile and she cackled with mirth.

'I'm glad you find it funny,' Vanessa said, and then reluctantly smiled back. It was hard to remain angry in the face of this woman's patience, and with a sigh she sat down again.

Before she could resume her spinning, a bell chimed in the courtyard and she glanced through the narrow window and saw Ramon de la Rivas by the fountain that stood in the centre of it. He was looking at the shimmer of water that poured from the mouth of a stone angel and it gave her a chance to study his profile. What an uncompromising one it was, with its high forehead, aquiline nose and thin lips. He could have been a model for a Modigliani or El Greco drawing, for they would both have had the same long lines as this six-foot specimen of virile manhood.

The bell chimed again and the man glanced at the house and the room where he knew Vanessa to be. She stepped quickly back from the window, even though he was too far away to see her. The bell must be a signal for lunch. She looked at her watch. It was two-thirty. No wonder she felt faint! Pointing at the dial, she smiled at Josefina and went to her room to wash her hands. Though she had only been at the spinning wheel a short time, the skin on her fingers was already chafed. Heaven knew what state her hands would be in after several hours of this work. With a toss of her head she went down to the courtyard, where her host was already standing by a small table set in the shade of a giant pot plant, whose flowers cast a pink glow—almost as if it were a lamp—around him.

'The colour comes from the leaves,' he said, seeing her glance at it. 'Although they look green, they give off a red reflection.'

'How unusual!'

'Many of our plants are unusual, señorita. But they are also beautiful. It is like my country itself.'

'I can't say I've found Peru beautiful,' she commented, and began to sip the iced soup that had been set before her. It was a spicy avocado cream and she would dearly have liked to know how it was made.

'I suppose you prefer the muted colours and scenery of a Constable type landscape?' he said.

'I'm not as insular as you make out, *señor*. I appreciate other cultures and other lands—but not when I'm a prisoner in them!'

'I knew we would get around to that.' He gave a slight smile. 'I would prefer it if you regarded yourself as my guest. It would make your stay here more pleasant.'

'A guest is free to come and go, *señor*, and since I'm not, I would rather stick to the truth and use the word "prisoner".'

His shrug indicated she could have it her own way, and they finished their first course without further conversation. The soup bowls were whisked away and a large dish of assorted cold meats was set in front of them, with several smaller ones filled with vegetables, diced and glistening with oil and lemon. It was very much a Spanish repast, though some of the side dishes were so hot and spicy that they brought tears to Vanessa's eyes. The man ate them with relish and even added more chilis to a bowl of tiny maize cobs. He not only had a will of iron but a cast-iron stomach too, she thought, and lowered her head quickly to hide her smile. But it was not quick enough, for he noticed it.

'Something amuses you?' he asked.

She hesitated, then said frankly: 'I'm amazed by the way you can eat whole lumps of chili. Even a speck of the powder burns off my tongue!'

'It's a matter of habit. You will also get used to them in time.'

'I hope I won't be here that long.'

He ignored the comment. 'How is the spinning going?'

'It isn't.'

'You'll soon learn. If Josefina cannot teach you, nobody can.'

'But saying she can't,' Vanessa persisted, 'will you keep me here for ever?'

The pupils of the brown eyes seemed to widen as they moved over her burnished hair and flushed cheeks to rest on her tremulously curved red mouth. 'It is an idea that hadn't occurred to me until now,' he murmured.

Fear rose in her. A deeper, more basic fear than her earlier one. In normal circumstances the look of desire on Ramón de la Rivas' face would have given her a sense of power and pleasure, but here, in the heart of this remote wilderness, it brought only the deepest unease.

'You haven't touched your wine,' he commented, and his long narrow hand pointed to the crystal goblet in front of her.

'A slave works better with a clear head,' she replied.

'You don't know the meaning of the word "slave" if you apply it to the work you've done this morning. Wait until the end of the week, *señorita*, then you'll know better what the word means!'

She rose and pushed back her chair. It grated loudly on the tiled floor. 'If you will excuse me, *señor*, I will resume work and leave you to finish your lunch in peace.'

Not waiting for his permission to go, she ran into the house.

Even during her short absence Josefina had spun a considerable amount of wool, and she vacated the seat for Vanessa to take it. With a sigh, Vanessa set to work. She was slightly more proficient this time, but still found it difficult to spin the thread for any length without breaking it. But the longer she worked the more accomplished she became, though the fibres rasped on her skin and made her wince.

It was only when specks of blood appeared on the wool that Josefina muttered loudly and stopped the wheel turning. Reaching out, she lifted up one of Vanessa's hands. The skin on some of the fingers had been rubbed raw and one was bleeding profusely. Josefina shook her head and went flat-footed from the room.

A few moments later she returned with another woman who looked at Vanessa's hands and also shook her head. Then the two of them went out and Vanessa closed her eyes and let her hands lie idly in her lap. They throbbed dully, but she was too tired to care. She had been spinning for more hours than she could count and daylight had already given way to dusk. The oil lamp had been lit but only shed a mellow radiance in the centre of the room, leaving the corners in shadow.

'What's wrong with your hands?'

The sharp voice of Ramon de la Rivas made her jerk her eyes open, and she saw him come over to her side and peer down at them. There was a lengthy pause before he spoke.

'I will put some cream on the broken skin,' he said in a curiously strained tone. 'Please come with me.'

Too tired to argue, she followed him up to the first floor and along the corridor in the opposite direction from her own room. Only as they reached another bedroom, its size and luxurious furnishing telling her it was his, did she stop and refuse to move further.

'I have no designs on your person,' he said crisply. 'But I keep all the medicines here.'

With eyes lowered she went into a large tiled bathroom. Mirrored cabinets lined one wall and he opened the first one to show a surprising display of medicaments. Without hesitation he took out a jar and opened it.

'Sit down,' he ordered.

Meekly she did so, seeing hundreds of reflections of herself in the intricately faceted mirrors that made up the walls on either side of the huge sunken bath. There was a sybaritic quality about the bathroom that surprised her, until she realised it was not as out of character as she had supposed. After all, a man who managed to drink perfectly chilled hock in the middle of the Andes was a man who liked the best of everything and would see he had it at all times.

'This may sting,' he said, and she looked at him uneasily. He was bending forward, his face close to hers. The yellow glints she had suspected in his eyes were now confirmed, and were like amber specks in agate.

'Shouldn't I wash my hands first?' she asked huskily.

'I don't want you to get water on them. Anyway, this ointment will act as a disinfectant.' With a surprisingly gentle touch he applied the unguent to her chafed fingers. 'Do you have any cotton gloves?' he asked and, as she nodded, said: 'Wear them during the night and all day tomorrow. I'm sorry you've had this trouble, Miss Wayne. I should have warned Josefina not to let you spin too fast. Her skin is like leather and she made no allowance for yours being soft.'

Vanessa rose and stared at him beseechingly. 'Please let me go back to Puno. I'll swear I'll try to contact Madame Delphine and . . .' Her voice trailed away as she saw the lines of his face harden. With a hopeless sigh she walked past him. 'You are a cruel man, señor.'

'And you are a clever woman. But it would take more than chafed hands to arouse my compassion.'

'You need a heart before you can have compassion,' she

said, 'and you *señor*, are completely heartless.'

Head high, she left him, but in the seclusion of her bed-room she gave way to tears. If only Delphine knew where she was! Agitatedly she paced the floor, wishing there was some way of contacting her. But there was no hope of contacting anyone in the next town, let alone England, and she knew she had only herself on whom to rely. If she could not escape from here on her own, she was doomed to be held captive for weeks.

Going to the window, she peered into the courtyard. On the far side there was a door that led to the exterior of the house and it was here that the Land Rover was parked. Excitement quickened her pulses. Her room was only one storey from the ground, but it was too high for her to jump. If she had a rope she could tie it to one of the wooden bed-posts and climb down. She had been a good gymnast at school and it would not be difficult to do. Except for the fact that she had no rope. Sheets, then. She ran to the bed. Yes, two sheets could be knotted together and would give enough length for her to jump safely the rest of the way.

She went to pull off the top sheet and stopped with a gasp of pain. It was impossible for her to climb anywhere if she could not use her hands. So *that* avenue of escape was barred. But not for ever. Once her fingers had healed she could still use it as a means of getting out. Meantime she must discover where Señor de la Rivas kept his car keys.

Encouraged by the knowledge that she would soon be able to make a bid for freedom, she slipped off her dress and lay down. But her right hand was throbbing painfully and made sleep impossible. It had been stupid of her not to realise that the rough wool would chafe her skin. Had she spun more slowly she would not have set up such friction. But thinking of the might-have-beens did not change the facts as they were now. She would be unable to work for three days at least, and this meant three more days here.

Impatiently she swung her feet to the ground. How incred-ible that she should be confined in this wilderness! If she had read of such a thing happening she would never have believed it. But then Ramon de la Rivas was a pretty unbelievable character. Curiosity stirred in her. How long had he lived in such solitary splendour, and what had made him leave Lima?

Was running this *hacienda* his sole occupation, or did he have other work? He was obviously rich, for this valley was well cultivated and would bring in a good living, but surely not enough to enable him to maintain this house and its servants? Still, labour was cheap in Peru and there was no shortage of men and women who would work merely in order to keep body and soul together.

Dusk gave way to darkness, and her hunger grew, making her regret the lunch she had left untasted. Next time she would learn to control her temper. Cutting off one's nose never spoilt anyone else's face. With a sigh she took off her cotton dress and hung it over a chair. It was limp and creased and would have to be ironed before she could put it on again. If only she had something else that was cool enough to wear. A wry smile curved her mouth. What sort of person was she that she could think about changing for dinner with her jailor! If she had any sense she would insist on being served in her room. She toyed with the idea and then dismissed it. Being alone for hours on end would depress her more than she was already. Besides, if she talked with the man she might glean something that would help her in her bid to escape.

Opening the hand-carved wardrobe, she looked at her meagre selection of clothes. Her coolest one—apart from the cotton—was a black woollen skirt and turquoise crêpe blouse. She put them on. The crêpe was heavy on her skin and she rolled up the sleeves as far as they would go. It made the blouse look workmanlike and she frowned at her reflection and rolled the sleeves down again. Yes, even though it was hot, it was better to wear it like this. She fumbled at the buttons on her cuff but could not do them up without making her hands throb; nor could she do her hair without a great deal of pain, and she brushed it loose and let it fall to her shoulders. The humidity made it wave and little fronds curled around her forehead and on her cheeks, robbing her of her usual smooth sophistication. No wonder Señor de la Rivas had thought she looked young! Impatiently she turned away from the mirror, slipped a handkerchief into the pocket of her skirt, and went downstairs.

All the rooms were deserted, though the dining room table was laid for two and the oil lamps were lit. She went in and paused by the window. The courtyard was drenched by moonlight, its colour transformed to black and white. It could have been a patio in any tropical country, and only the Indian man crossing it, his poncho masking the top of his body, told her it was Peru. The hairs on the nape of her neck stiffened and, though there had been no sound, she knew she was being watched. Swiftly she turned. The tall Peruvian stood watching her, his height and breadth of shoulder diminishing the width of the doorway.

'I didn't know you were down,' he said softly. 'Please join me in the library for a drink.'

She wanted to tell him she did not wish to drink with her captor, but knew that if she did, she would be unable to dine with him either. Yet frustration acted like a spur on her tongue and the words tumbled out.

'I prefer to wait in here, señor. I only drink with my friends.'

The words shivered into a silence that lengthened and became almost tangibly icy; as if his aristocratic blood had frozen in his veins at her rudeness.

'You must forgive me, señor,' she explained, 'but I'm not sophisticated enough to pretend to a friendship I don't feel.'

'If you could accept my criticism of your behaviour, you would stop regarding me as your enemy.'

'Then why can't you accept my word that I'm not Delphine's partner?' she said passionately. 'Then neither of us would be standing here arguing.'

'There is no argument.' He stepped into the room and pulled at the silver tassel hanging beside the door. 'If you do not wish to drink with me, we will dine at once.'

'Let me go,' she begged.

'No!'

The word was like a lash on her skin, but her bitter retort died in her throat as two servants entered bearing large silver tureens.

Dinner was considerably more elaborate than lunch, the meats and vegetables sufficiently varied to make her wonder how he obtained such delicious things in the depths of the wilderness. As if he guessed her thoughts he told her something of his way of life, speaking as courteously as if they were genuinely host and guest.

Vanessa tried to look uninterested, but he was too good a raconteur not to capture her attention and she was soon enthralled by the way in which he brought to life the history of this remote property.

'For the first hundred years that my ancestors lived here,' he said as the main dishes were cleared away and individual bowls of fruit were set before them, 'they did nothing except run the *hacienda* and exploit the Indians. Then the oldest son fell in love with an Indian girl. His father forbade the marriage and sent the girl away to Lima, but what he did not know was that his son gave her money and arranged for her to stay at a convent and be educated. For ten years they were apart—until the father died—and only then did he bring back the girl and marry her.'

'Did he really?' Despite herself, Vanessa was moved by the story.

'Not only that,' the man replied, 'but she bore him nine sons—one of whom was my grandfather.' He touched his wine glass, his long fingers as slender as the stem. 'So you see there is Indian blood in me. Considerably diluted by now, but there, nonetheless.'

'I'm sure the same thing applies in many of your noble families,' she said.

'But it would be denied.'

'You don't deny it, *señor*.'

'Because I see no shame in it.' He eyed her keenly. 'I told you the story in the hope of making you understand why I've set myself up as guardian for these people. Someone has to start caring *actively*, Miss Wayne, and fate has decreed it to be me.'

'I don't need a reason to understand why you're kind to the Indians,' she said quickly.

'Kind?' It was almost a shout. '*Dios!* I'm not doing what I do out of kindness, but because I value the worth of a human being! If you cannot see that for yourself . . .' With an effort he remained silent, then he looked at the fruit bowl in front of her. 'You do not want any?'

'No, thank you, *señor*.'

Silently he took a mango and peeled it. Vanessa watched his fingers manipulate the silver-handled knife and appreciated the deft swiftness of his movement. As if aware of being watched he looked up, and the anger in his face died away as their eyes met.

'These are grown on my land,' he explained. 'You should try one. They are——' Again he stopped, but this time in contrition. 'How stupid I am! How can you eat fruit if you can't use your hands and peel it? Come, tell me what you want and I will do it for you.'

'I don't wish for anything more, *señor*.'

'An apple perhaps, or a peach? Look, it has the same bloom as the one on your cheeks.'

She trembled and coloured, then pleasure was overtaken by shame. How dare he compliment her as if she were a favoured guest when he was keeping her here by force?

'I don't want anything,' she choked, jumping to her feet. 'If you'll excuse me, *señor*, I'd like to go to my room.'

He leaned back in his chair, once more disdainful of her. 'You are free to retire whenever you wish.'

Only in the solitude of her room did her temper abate. Yet in all honesty she had to admit it was not the compliment that had upset her as much as her reaction to it. Anger, yes, but worse than that—and far stronger—had been the swift thrill his words had aroused. She tried to stop thinking of it, but it was impossible; so she sat by the window and determinedly tried to reason away her reactions.

It was natural for her to have been emotionally aroused by his compliments. Apart from the servants, they were alone together in a house miles from civilisation. In such circumstances most men would find her desirable, and this one in particular had the virility and conquering spirit of his forefathers. Because of this, only an old woman or a stupid one would fail to be afraid. And it was this fear that had made her react with such emotion to his compliment. It had nothing to do with his being young and handsome. Nothing whatever.

CHAPTER SIX

In the morning the Indian woman who had served Vanessa her morning coffee since she had arrived here brought her breakfast on a tray. It seemed that because of her hands she was being treated like an invalid. She was glad she had no need to get up and have breakfast in the patio, for her right hand was still painful and had awakened her several times in the night, though now it had settled into a dull throb.

After washing her face with cool water, she returned to bed and looked at her tray. There was a boiled egg, the inevitable maize cakes and a bowl of some strange-looking cereal together with a small jug of milk and a delicately fluted dish of honey. As well as coffee there was a thermos of creamy hot chocolate and, beside it, a small silver bowl holding a perfectly ripened peach. Someone had gone to a great deal of trouble to prepare her breakfast this morning and, knowing it could only have been on the instructions of one man, Vanessa was perturbed.

His presence hovered around her—almost as if his spirit were in the room—and his name came so clearly into her mind that she said it aloud—Ramon de la Rivas—then looked round guiltily in case anyone could have heard her.

Dismayed that he was continuing to occupy her mind, she concentrated on her breakfast, enjoying the cereal and egg and finding the thin maize cakes far more delectable with honey on them. The chocolate was far nicer than the coffee, which she still found too strong for her taste, and she drained the thermos before pushing the tray aside and resting back on the pillows. It was a sultry day and no breeze stirred the white silk drapes at the window. Yet the heavy stone walls kept out a considerable amount of the heat and made the air-conditioning unnecessary.

Thinking of the heat made her think of her wardrobe. There was no help but to wear the cotton dress once more. She pulled a face at the prospect. It was none too clean after having been worn yesterday, but she had been unable to wash it with one hand and had not thought to give it to one

77

of the servants. She was trying to think of an alternative when there was a rap on the door and a young maid called Maria came in carrying a pile of clothes in assorted colours, which she started to lay out on the bed.

Vanessa pulled her feet under her and knelt up, staring in bewilderment at the beautiful garments—some silk, some cotton; some in plain styles and many in elaborate ones for evening. None of them were new, but they were all clean and in current fashion. Did the Señor have a wife after all? She touched one of the dresses and looked at the girl.

'Señora de la Rivas?' she asked.

A spate of dialect was Vanessa's only answer and she made no attempt to follow it. But the shake of her head told Maria she had not been understood and the girl lifted her shoulders and glided out.

Left alone, Vanessa examined the clothes carefully, astonished to find that many of them were exquisitely made copies of last season's better known designs. She lifted up one in pinky beige cream silk, almost the colour of her skin, and held it against her. It seemed to be her size, and she doffed her nightgown and slipped it on. It was slightly tight across her breasts and too large in the waist, but otherwise it fitted quite well.

The door opened and Maria came back with a photograph in a silver frame. She held it out and Vanessa saw a picture of Ramon de la Rivas. He was staring into the camera lens with his usual haughty look, but his arm was thrown affectionately over the shoulders of a slim, delicately featured young woman whose black hair and dark eyes proclaimed her Spanish heritage. There was something familiar about the shape of her eyes and nose, and Vanessa tilted the picture to get a better look at it. Then her eyes returned to the man. Even in a photograph his strong personality was evident. He was leaning against a stone column and gave the impression that at a given word he was going to walk out of the frame. It was a silly thought and she hurriedly returned the photograph to the maid.

'Señora Almara.' Maria pointed to the girl. 'Señorita de la Rivas. Señora Almara.'

Vanessa smiled her understanding, and Maria smiled back and went out.

So the clothes belonged to her jailor's sister. The fact that they were still in style indicated she came here frequently and, as they had been left here, also meant she was likely to return soon. It was too much to expect this would be within a few days, but at least it gave Vanessa hope that she would not be incarcerated here for ever.

Taking off the dress, she went into the bathroom to shower, then with a fluffy towelling coat wrapped around her, she sat by the window to dry. She was still there when Maria came back for the third time and, by mime, indicated that she was to help Vanessa dress.

Vanessa knew that, as with the breakfast, this was the order of Señor de la Rivas, and she was surprised that he had given any thought to her predicament. Most men would have been unaware of the difficulty of dressing with one hand, and it was doubly odd that he should be concerned with the welfare of someone whose business ethics he despised.

With Maria's deft help she was soon wearing a sleeveless blue dress made in some silky knit fibre, delicate as a cobweb. It too was an exquisite copy of a Missoni and she would dearly have liked to know who had made it. But it was useless to ask Maria, who was now busily brushing Vanessa's hair and giving pleased little grunts as she lifted up several strands and examined the colour.

Vanessa picked up a velvet ribbon from the dressing table and held it out to show she wished to have her hair tied back, but Maria frowned and, from a pocket in her voluminous skirt, took out a silver hair buckle. It was inset with turquoise in a typical Aztec design and was far nicer than anything Vanessa had seen in the markets.

'It's lovely,' she murmured.

Maria smiled at the tone and gathered up the rich, titian-coloured hair. Skilfully she slipped it through the silver buckle which lay lightly on the nape of Vanessa's neck, then allowed the hair to fall free.

With her hair completely caught back from her face, its bone structure was far more evident, as were the shadows of fatigue under her blue eyes. Defiantly she put on lipstick, applying more colour than she usually did. Then with a smile of thanks at Maria, she stood up.

Her blue skirt swished gracefully around her legs as she

made her way down to the hall, and she was unaware of the lovely picture she made against the dark stone walls, with her hair glowing like burgundy from its vigorous brushing and her blue eyes violet-shadowed and still languorous with fatigue.

The man coming in from the courtyard gave a half-in-drawn breath as he saw her, then stopped to watch her descend until her slender blue image was reflected in his dark eyes.

'Good morning,' he said courteously. 'How are your hands?'

'Improving.'

She was aware of the cotton gloves covering them, but as she went to put them behind her back he shook his head.

'No. I wish to change the dressings. Please come with me.'

She was still reluctant to go to his bedroom and was relieved when he led her into an oval-shaped room furnished with delightful pieces in Louis Quinze. It was so different from the other rooms that she could not hide her surprise.

'You like it?' he asked.

'Who wouldn't?'

She eyed the beautiful furniture: the writing desk inlaid with marquetry, as were several tiny round tables on which stood numerous photographs in silver frames. There were a couple of two-seater settees and several elbow chairs—antique, but still in excellent condition, their gilded arms and legs rosy with the patina of age. There was also a small armchair upholstered in blue and looking far more comfortable than the rest, and it was to this that he pointed.

Feeling almost as if she were an interloper, Vanessa perched on it. There was a gentle fragrance in the room—almost as if its owner's presence were still within it—and she gave a little shiver.

'You are cold?' he asked.

'No. I—I felt as if someone were here.'

'My mother,' he said instantly. 'This was her room. She didn't like the *hacienda*, so my father had the idea of building this room for her. All the others are square or rectangular, but this one is octagonal, like one of the rooms in the house where she was born. He even had the furniture shipped over from Limoges.'

'Your mother was French?'

'Yes. My father met her in Paris. For some years he was the Ambassador there.'

'A different life from this,' she murmured. 'I'm not surprised she was unhappy here.'

'My mother was never unhappy,' he corrected gravely. 'As long as she and my father were together, she was content. But he knew she had wonderful memories of her childhood home, and to help keep them alive, he created this room for her. He had it done while they were living in Lima, and she found it waiting for her on her return.'

'He must have loved her very much to have gone to so much trouble,' said Vanessa.

'He worshipped her.' There was a gentle tone in the man's voice that gave it the resonance of a cello. 'Everyone who knew my mother felt the same way about her. She was a rare woman.'

'Rare?'

'In that she put her husband and family before anything else. She would not have understood the modern girl's desire for a career, nor have wanted to—how do you say in the West—done her own thing. In your terms, Miss Wayne, she was unliberated.'

'On the contrary,' Vanessa corrected, 'she was completely liberated. She was a fulfilled woman who did not hanker to do anything other than what she was doing. In my terms—in today's terms if you like—she was very much liberated. Feminists aren't forcing women to do what they don't want to do, señor. They're merely saying that women should have the same opportunities as men.'

'Until men can bear children, they will never have the same opportunities!' he retorted. 'Nature has given woman a different outlook on life, and she is foolish to ignore it. Babies need a mother and——'

'Babies need mothering,' Vanessa interrupted. 'That isn't the same thing.'

'Would you want your babies to be loved by a surrogate mother?' he demanded.

She clasped her lips tightly together. His phraseology told her she was dealing with a man who knew something about the subject on which he was talking—a rare event these days

—and though she would have enjoyed the argument that would have developed from giving him an answer, she was in no mood to put their relationship on such a level. He was her jailor and, as such, her enemy.

'I see you cannot answer my question,' he said with a smile. 'You should think about your attitudes more carefully, Miss Wayne. Perhaps you are not as liberated as you think!'

'Too liberated to see marriage as a prison! Babies should enrich a woman's life, not diminish it—and if the father takes equal responsibility for them, then this is possible.'

'Most things are possible,' came the reply, 'but not all are logical. Tell me,' he went on, 'what would you do if you were married and your husband's work took him to some remote part of the world that made it impossible for you to continue your career? Would you go with him or would you part?'

Knowing that if she continued to remain silent he would see it as his victory, Vanessa was forced into a reply.

'If I loved him, I would want to be with him. Equally, if he loved me he would not wish me to sacrifice my *own* happiness for *his*. You see, *señor*, I don't believe I could love a man unless we had the same fundamental principles. And that means a marriage where husband and wife are equal.'

The amber glints in the dark eyes were noticeable. 'An excellent wish, *señorita*. I hope it is not a too ambitious one.'

She lowered her eyes to the carpet. It was not one of the bright Peruvian ones but an Aubusson whose colours had been dimmed by the passage of time.

'Please take off your gloves,' the man said.

She did so and he gave a low imprecation. Glancing up, she saw he had gone pale beneath his tan. She looked at her right hand and could understand why. The skin was a mass of blisters and some of the fingers were badly swollen.

'I'm not surprised there are shadows beneath your eyes,' he said quietly. 'You must be in considerable pain.'

'It isn't as bad as it looks.'

'Nevertheless I want to give you an antibiotic injection.'

'You?' She stared directly at him: blue eyes locking with brown.

'I did three years at medical school before I decided that the life of a doctor was not for me. But I have retained the knowledge I acquired there. It comes in useful during my stay here.'

'I don't think an injection is necessary,' Vanessa said.

'You might get blood poisoning. Don't be afraid, Miss Wayne, I won't hurt you.'

'I'm not afraid,' she retorted, but could not explain why she was reluctant for him to do as he wished.

'I'll prepare the injection,' he said, and left her, returning in a few minutes with a plastic wrapped syringe and a phial of colourless fluid.

'Your arm or the top of your leg?' he asked unceremoniously.

'My arm, of course,' she snapped, and could have sworn she saw the suspicion of a smile curve his mouth.

But deftly he pushed up her sleeve, rubbed alcohol on her skin and plunged the needle into her forearm. It was done with the swift competence she had come to expect from him.

'Good girl,' he said in a surprisingly gentle voice. 'Now I'll put on another type of cream. It's a little sticky, but it will help the blisters.' As he spoke he liberally applied a gooey fluid to both hands, then swathed them in gauze and put on the gloves, tying each one securely around her wrist.

'I feel as if I'm getting ready for a boxing match,' she said.

'For the next few days you will have to rely on your tongue!' He held open the door for her and she rose. He saw the slowness of her movement and gave her a look of concern. 'You are unwell? You wish to remain here?'

'I am quite well, señor, but I would very much like to remain here. I think this room is beautiful and . . .' She went to the door. 'But forgive me, I am your prisoner and will do as you say.'

'Dios!' It was an exclamation of irritability. 'Can you not forget that you are here because . . .' His voice trailed away as he realised the impossibility of the suggestion he had been about to make. 'The injury to your hands will only delay your departure for a few days. Josefina has assured me you are an apt pupil and that with her help, you should complete your tasks easily.'

'I'm glad you have enough of a conscience to let her help me,' Vanessa said icily. 'It's a pity your conscience won't let me go.'

'Perhaps it's because I regard you as my guest and not my prisoner,' he said softly. 'You are free to come to this room whenever you wish, but at the moment I would like you to come with me. I have planned a tour for you which I hope you will find interesting.'

With a shrug she went with him to the Land Rover.

'You will need to take something warm to wear,' he said, and spoke to the young Indian boy who had followed them.

The lad ran off and Vanessa wandered round to the far side of the vehicle, anxious to put some distance between herself and the tall, bronzed man who kept eyeing her with a glittering look that she found disturbing.

The boy returned with a snow white fur coat and she gaped at it. 'Surely I won't want to wear that?'

'You will.' Ramon de la Rivas tossed the coat into the back of the car with total disregard for its pristine whiteness. Then he went round the side to help her in. Avoiding his hand, she jumped in unaided.

'Are all European women so independent?' he enquired, letting in the clutch vigorously.

'Do you mean there are some types of women you don't know?' she asked sarcastically. 'I thought you were an expert on everything!'

'Emancipated women are not my type.'

She bit her lip and concentrated on the view. They were moving away from the valley and she was disappointed.

'I thought we were going down to the settlement again, señor.'

'You would hardly need a fur coat for that. No, today I intend to show you another part of my country.'

'As compensation for my wounds?' she asked sweetly.

'Do not try my patience too far, señorita,' he said through barely open lips, 'the de la Rivas men are known for their temper.'

'And the de la Rivas women?'

'For their docility.'

'They would have to be docile to be——' She stopped in time. She was not going to enter into a slanging match with this haughty savage.

They were climbing steeply and she knew they were travelling the road she had come along with Manuel two nights ago.

Had she only been here such a short while? It seemed as if it was weeks. She thought of Delphine and knew it would be another week at least before the woman began to wonder what had happened to her.

She glanced at her bandaged hands and tried to flex the fingers. The movement increased the throbbing and she winced.

'Keep them still,' the man at her side commanded, making her think he must have eyes everywhere, for she had judged him to be giving his full attention to the road.

'How long will it be before I can use them?' she asked.

'I don't know. But when they *are* healed I won't let you return to spinning. The little that you did will suffice to remind you of the painful outcome it can have.'

'Ah yes,' she said, still sarcastic. 'I'm supposed to suffer, in order to appreciate the value of the things I want to buy.'

'Can you think of a better way of learning how to appreciate them?'

'Since I already appreciate them,' she flared, 'the whole exercise is a waste of time.'

'Then show your appreciation by paying the prices I have asked.'

'Would you let me go then?'

'Naturally.'

It was a great temptation to tell him she would do as he wished and had she been her own boss—as he believed—she would have done it long ago. In fact she would have paid more without being asked, rather than feel she was taking advantage of people who lived in such poverty. But unfortunately she could not spend any more money until she had obtained her employer's permission.

'I cannot do it, *señor*. I must talk to Madame Delphine first.'

He stepped fiercely on the accelerator and the Land Rover shot forward. 'So you still persist with that fable,' he ground out. 'Well, on your own head be it!'

The wheels screeched as they took a bend without lowering speed and, unable to use her hands to steady herself, her body was shaken up and down like beans in a bag.

Higher and higher they climbed, though it was a considerable time before they left the warmth of the valley behind and reached the grass-covered plateau. It was the first time she had seen this part of the country in the daylight, for it had been dark when Manuel had driven her through it, and she realised it was a depression of land set between the mountains and forming a wide basin that served as grazing land for what seemed to be thousands of sheep. Far away on the horizon she glimpsed a huddle of stone houses and knew it was the settlement of the Indians who tended these herds.

'Is this your property too?' she asked.

'Yes. This part of Peru is mainly given over to sheep rearing. We produce some of the softest wool in the world.'

'I know. I had intended to visit a couple of textile factories.'

'*Had* intended?'

She tilted her chin. 'The moment you set me free, I'm going home. The quicker I leave Peru, the better.'

He looked so grim that Vanessa knew she had displeased him. But she was beyond caring what he thought of her and, throwing caution to the winds, said: 'You will find, *señor*, that though keeping me here may give you personal satisfaction, it will not bring one extra *sol* to your people.'

'I'm sorry you're so delighted to admit you're a woman who can learn nothing from experience. I should have thought even the most stupid female could do that!'

Awarding him this particular round, she looked out of the window.

'You had better put the coat on,' he said. 'It's getting cold.'

She half turned to say she wasn't cold when she realised she was, and that it was only her temper which had prevented her from noticing it. She reached into the back and draped the coat around her.

'Put it on,' he said, and slowed slightly in order to enable her to do so without bumping around.

The coat was lightweight but exceptionally warm, and made of a fur she did not recognise. She refused to ask him what it was, despite her curiosity and, snuggling into it, stared silently ahead. But it was difficult to remain silent when the man beside her seemed to shake off his anger and started to tell her more of the history of his country.

'The Indians here are the direct descendants of the Incas.

I take it you know something of them?'

'Only that they worshipped the sun and ruled Peru in the eleventh century.'

'They were here until Pizarro conquered them in 1531,' he corrected. 'The Inca leaders were dictators—but benevolent ones. In a way they were too good, for the mass of Indians relied on them so much that they lost all their own initiative.'

'Worshipping the master,' she said very quietly, and knew he took the point from the way his narrow, strong hands tightened on the wheel.

'That's why the Indians submitted so easily to Spanish rule,' he continued smoothly. 'And the Spaniards treated them abominably.'.

'I'm surprised you don't find an excuse for them.'

'I can't find any that would ring true. Had I been born at that time, I would have renounced my birthright!'

The vehemence in his voice made it clear he meant every word, and unwillingly she warmed to him.

'Their situation hasn't improved all that much, has it?' she ventured.

'It's considerably better than it was twenty years ago. But the main enemy of progress is Peru itself. It's almost like three separate countries. There's the coastal region—which is desert interspersed with rivers—then there's the Andes and beyond them the jungle. That's where much of our wealth lies—if only we can make it approachable and habitable!'

'But roads are being built,' she said. 'Don told me.'

'Don?' The question was sharp.

'Don Riversdale. I met him on the plane coming over. He's in the Trade Section of the British Embassy. I do appreciate the problems of your country, señor, even though you think I'm heartless.'

He was silent and she hoped he was feeling small—mentally if not physically. Quickly she darted him a look; tall and loose-limbed, he filled the jeep with his presence; as much in control of the vehicle as he was of herself. Too aware of him, Vanessa plunged into conversation.

'How many people live in the high sierras compared with the cities?'

'Three-quarters of the population live here,' he replied.

'But many of them go into the towns hoping to find work. The Government wants people to remain here and they're trying to bring industry in, but it's a slow process.'

'Are there many *haciendas* like yours?'

'Most of them are co-operatives now—run and owned by the Indians. But they still use primitive farming methods, so the potential of the land isn't being wasted.'

'How have *you* managed to prevent *your hacienda* from being taken over?' she asked.

'I run it well and I pay well.'

She felt she had been subtly reprimanded and she lapsed into silence.

Their journey continued and looked as if it could continue for days, so vast was the expanse of land around her and so distant the ring of snow-capped mountains. Despite her fur coat she was not over-warm; the air was crisp as fresh-picked celery, and had the clear headiness of wine; all she needed was some cheese, she thought fancifully, and she could have an imaginary meal! Her mouth watered and she realised she was hungry. But she was loath to ask if they were returning to the house for lunch, sure that to do so would evoke some biting response from Ramon de la Rivas.

'Time to eat,' he said, as if he had read her mind, and brought the jeep to a halt. From the back seat he lifted up a hamper and flung back the lid to take out plastic plates and cups. 'I regret it isn't china and glass, but on these bumpy roads they tend to break.'

'I couldn't care less about the crockery,' she replied, 'as long as the food isn't plastic!'

'That I can guarantee.' He smiled at her. 'I'm glad you're hungry. It's a sign that the fever isn't winning.'

His reference to her hands showed he was still worried about her, and she was sorry she had not played it up more. If she had pretended to be suffering badly he might have let her return to Puno. But it was too late for that now and she settled instead for a tremulous sigh—as if to indicate frailty—before eating with gusto the cold chicken and salad which he piled on to her plate. Following this came a sweet almond cake, washed down for him with strong black coffee and for herself by hot chocolate.

'You must thank my sister for this,' he said, replenishing

her cup. 'She always insists we have a stock of chocolate in case she arrives unexpectedly.'

Vanessa was glad he had referred to his sister, for it gave her the chance to thank him for the dresses.

'It is better for you to wear them than to die of heat-stroke,' he replied.

It was not the most gracious of answers, but since she had never been gracious to him either, she was not surprised.

She watched him as he repacked the crockery and cutlery and then took a long dark cheroot from his inside pocket.

'You permit me to smoke?' he asked politely.

Her glance took in the vast wilderness around them. 'I don't think you'll pollute the atmosphere of our little room, *señor*.'

His laughter, deep and mellow, was the first she had heard from him and she liked the sound of it, particularly the way in which humour changed his face, releasing the tight line of his mouth and placing little ones around his eyes.

'I'm afraid I do not have a cigarette to offer you, Miss Wayne.'

'I don't smoke, thank you.'

'That is good.'

She wished immediately that she did smoke, and her expression gave her away, for he chuckled.

'Sometimes I find you very transparent, *señorita*,' he observed.

'I can't say the same about you.'

'I have learned how to disguise my feelings. It is a necessity for a highly eligible bachelor.'

Her fingers itched to slap him, but she said coolly: 'I hadn't realised conceit was another of your characteristics.'

'Another?' His well-shaped eyebrows rose like dark wings. 'I would be interested to have you enumerate the others.'

'Bossiness, quick temper, autocracy, rigidity,' she said without pause. 'Do you wish me to go on?'

'No, thank you.' He blew out a smoke ring, tilting his head back to do so and giving her a glimpse of his throat, firm and brown. He wore no tie, but his shirt was buttoned against the wind and she could not see the medallion that she knew lay upon his chest. All at once he straightened and stared directly into her face. His eyes were so near her own that she saw the yellow flecks in them.

'Tell me my good points, Miss Wayne.'

Warmth stole over her and she hoped it was not apparent in her face. 'I—er—I don't know them,' she stammered.

'I must see what I can do to remedy that.'

She was about to make an angry retort when caution kept her quiet. Her only way of escaping from him was to get him off his guard. And the only way of doing that was to have him relax. With an effort she forced a smile to her lips and was triumphant when she saw him return it even more warmly.

Whistling softly—always a sure sign that a man was feeling pleased with himself—he set the jeep in motion and headed towards the Indian settlement.

Several of the women were busy about their daily tasks. They wore voluminous black skirt and tops, crowned by the ubiquitous high bowler hat, which gave them the appearance of being men in drag. But the children were delightful; chubby-faced and almond-eyed, and all of them greeting the man with great affection. Vanessa wished she could talk to them in their own language, but had to be content with smiling and listening, managing to follow what was being said merely by looking at Ramon de la Rivas' face. It held compassion when he enquired after someone's health, amusement when a recalcitrant child was dragged forward and some misdemeanour recounted to him, and deep pleasure when a new-born infant was presented to him to admire.

It was dusk when they finally returned to the *hacienda*. Here the air was heavy and damp and Vanessa had long since discarded the fur coat. She was extremely tired: not so much from the long drive but from having to hold her body taut against the buffeting of the jeep.

But Ramon de la Rivas strode towards the front door with the same vitality with which he had left it; only pausing to greet the labrador that came bounding up to him.

'Hello, Sinbad,' he said. 'Did you miss me?'

The dog wagged his tail furiously, then favoured Vanessa with a lick.

'He's lovely,' she remarked, patting his head. 'Why do you call him Sinbad?'

'Because like the sailor, he has a bitch in every port!'

She walked quickly ahead, but he caught up with her in the hall.

'I did not mean the remark to offend you,' he apologised.

'It didn't. But'—she hesitated—'it's out of character for you.'

'How so?'

She hesitated, remembering her earlier vow to lull his watchfulness over her. 'You're so much the Spanish Grandee,' she explained, 'that I see you as being aloof from—from . . .' Heavens, she thought, this is getting worse and worse.

'Sex?' he finished for her calmly. 'Even a Spanish Grandee is subject to the rule of nature.'

'Rule of nature?'

'Of course. That is all the sex urge is. Nature's way of ensuring the species.'

'Oh!' She swung away from him, but with unexpected swiftness he was ahead of her, stopping her in mid-flight.

'That doesn't mean I rule out love, Miss Wayne. But I do not happen to confuse it with desire.'

He fell silent but did not step away from her, so that short of pushing past him, she had to remain where she was.

'I can assure you I meant no disrespect when I made that joke about Sinbad,' he said seriously.

'Thank you, señor.'

He moved slightly to let her pass him.

'You look fatigued, Miss Wayne. I suggest you rest for a few hours. I will delay dinner until ten.'

'That's very late for you. Please don't bother.'

'It's no bother. In Lima I often dine later.'

'I can have something to eat in my room,' she persisted.

'Are you afraid to dine with me?'

Here was her chance to disarm him, and with an effort she took it. 'Of course not, señor, but I don't want to disturb your routine.'

'A beautiful woman cannot help causing a disturbance,' he said softly, the amber glints predominant in his eyes. 'Until later, señorita. Rest well.'

Feeling that this enigmatic foreigner was more in charge of the situation than she was, Vanessa mounted the stairs.

She was nearly at the top when his whispered, '*Señorita*?' made her turn.

'Yes?' she asked.

'You have no need to fear me as a man. You are a guest in my home and I never abuse my privilege as a host.'

Only as she felt her body sag did she realise how tense she had been. 'Thank you, *señor*. You have set my mind at rest.'

CHAPTER SEVEN

VANESSA could not fault Ramon de la Rivas' behaviour during the next few days. He was such an entertaining and kindly host that there were times when she forgot she was being held here against her will.

Life at the *hacienda* was idyllic, for though miles from civilisation, it was equipped with every luxury one could desire. Oil lamps might light the rooms. but that was only because the owner preferred their mellow light to the harshness of electricity; and a large dynamo powered the modern equipment in the kitchen, the stereo in the library, the air-conditioning and the piping hot water that flowed through the excellent plumbing.

The servants were all Indian except for the Spanish chef, who had been with his employer for many years and accompanied him to Lima when he lived there. All his employees doted on him, and watching the way he spoke to them and listened attentively when *they* spoke to him, Vanessa could appreciate why.

From the beginning she had known that Ramon Carlos Miguel Santos de la Rivas was a man of considerable charm, but now she was finding the charm being directed upon herself. She wanted to run away from it but was forced to pretend she was disarmed by it, for only by doing so could she disarm *him* and effect her freedom.

Yet the passing of the days lessened her desire to leave, and she was reminded of the Music Makers, though the stream by which she was sitting was not a desolate one but the rushing waters of the melting Andean snows.

Her injured hands had healed sufficiently for her to discard her bandages and gloves, and on the fifth day she was able to use them properly. This reminded her that she had been living here for nearly a week—time enough for Delphine to start worrying why there had been no word from her. Even though the woman was convalescing, surely she would be concerned at her employee's silence? But would she do anything about it, or would she wait another week in the belief that Vanessa was in some remote Peruvian village buying up more bargains? Somehow it was hard to see Delphine worrying about anyone but herself at the moment, and Vanessa knew it might be some time before the woman became sufficiently worried to contact the British Embassy in Lima. But even then, how could anyone trace her?

She suddenly thought of Don. He was expecting her back in Lima this weekend and, when she did not arrive, might try to discover what had happened to her. She had told him where she was staying in Puno and it was possible he would telephone her there. What would he do when they told him she was a guest of Señor de la Rivas? She could imagine the Peruvian's dismay if Don contacted her here! On the other hand Don might think she had made friends with some local people and was staying with them for a holiday. This being the case, he could decide to wait another week.

The more she thought about it the more she knew she had to make her own efforts to escape. Unless she did, she would be so beguiled by this earthly paradise that she would never want to leave it. She had grown to enjoy the hot days and warm evenings; being waited on by countless servants who seemed to know what she wanted before she even knew it herself. But above all, she enjoyed the company of the man who was keeping her captive, the savage aristocrat who was proving himself to be a gentle conqueror.

No man could have been kinder to her than Ramon de la Rivas had been these past few days, and she would not have been a woman had she not noticed the way his eyes brightened as she came to him each morning, fresh as a daisy in crisply starched cotton, or at night, languorous in gossamer silk. But not once had she felt any fear of him. He had said she was safe and she believed him. Even when she had seen the pulse beating in his temple or watched his hands clench tightly as she had said something provocative, she had not been afraid.

She thought of this as she went down to dinner on the Friday, exactly eight days after being brought here. As usual her host was waiting for her, but this time he was at the foot of the stairs, as if impatient to see her. The narrowing of his eyes as they rested on her told her she had made a wise choice in the hyacinth blue silk. It was less soignée than most of his sister's evening clothes, and to complement the simple style she had let her hair fall loosely around her face like a wine-dark cloud.

'You are always prompt,' he said. 'It is an unusual characteristic in a woman.'

'Not in a business woman,' she replied, and saw his lips tighten as if he found it displeasing to think of her as such. But then the women in his circle doubtless had no need to work—nor any inclination to do so. They were probably happy occupying their time with domesticity or socialising. It was a way of life that would have bored her to tears, but she was wise enough not to say so.

As always, dinner was perfect and, grown more used to spicier food, Vanessa approached it in a way she could not have done when she had first arrived. Afterwards they relaxed in the *sala*, a rectangular room furnished with many easy chairs and settees. It had less wooden furniture than the other rooms and, in consequence, was not as sombre-looking.

'Would you care for some music?' her host enquired and, at her nod, turned a switch that flooded the room with sound.

There must have been four speakers, skilfully placed, to give such exquisite reality to Vivaldi's *The Seasons*, and she listened enraptured, conscious of nothing except the music.

As it came to an end, both she and the man rose simultaneously. The movement brought them face to face, their bodies so close that had she drawn a deep breath her breasts would have touched his jacket. His eyes dilated, but he kept his control, though the effort tautened his face. For the space of a heartbeat their gaze met and held. Vanessa longed for him to make the infinitesimal movement that would bring her into his arms, yet was too afraid to give any indication of it, and she stood stiffly—as if to attention—only relaxing as, with a polite murmur, he stepped back and went over to the row of cassettes ranged on a shelf along one wall.

'Would you care to choose the next piece?' he asked.

Jerkily she followed him and blindly reached out for a tape. He took it, glanced at it and half smiled.

'So this is how you see yourself? You must tell me how many nights are left.'

Unwilling to admit she had chosen the music at random, she turned away and sat down. But as the first dulcet strains seeped around her, she knew what she meant. Folly of follies! What unkind god had guided her fingers to *Scheherezade*— the story of the slave girl who, for a thousand and one nights had spun a fairy tale to her Sultan, knowing that her life depended on keeping him amused until dawn.

Cheeks burning, she refused to look his way, and only after long moments had passed did she dare to do so. His lids were lowered, but she was not sure if his eyes were closed completely. His arms were on his chair, his hands loose, the fingers long and uncurled. He wore no rings on them and even his watch strap was a thin band of black leather. Tonight he had donned black corded trousers and a ruffled white shirt, the collar open and tieless. It was an exotic shirt and the red cummerbund that gripped his waist gave him the air of a matador. It was easy to visualise him in a bull ring, scarlet cape in hand, long legs and hard-muscled thighs swiftly evading the bull's horns.

With a swiftness that took her by surprise, his lids lifted and his eyes stared directly into hers.

'Scheherezade,' he said softly. 'It's a fitting name for you.'

'I prefer my own.'

'Vanessa.' It was the first time he had said it and he lengthened the second vowel. 'Vanessa,' he repeated, and continued to look at her.

There was a brooding quality about him that made her feel as if the breath were being squeezed from her body. He had not put a hand on her, yet she felt as if his fingers were caressing her skin; as if his mouth was touching hers. Her scalp tingled and she stood up.

'I'm going to bed, *señor*. It's late and I'm tired.'

'It is not late and you are not tired,' he replied. 'But by all means go to bed.' He rose too but remained by his chair.

'There are times when it is better to be safe than sorry, and tonight is one of them.'

She did not need to ask what he meant—her heart was telling her all too clearly—and with a tremulous smile she went from the room.

For a moment in the corridor she stood leaning against a wall, then ran swiftly to the hall. For no reason her glance fell upon the heavily carved table that stood there. On a silver dish lay a bunch of keys. She stopped running and looked at them. Then glancing over her shoulder to make sure Ramon de la Rivas had not followed her, she went closer and picked them up. Yes, they were the keys he always carried on a chain around his waist. She remembered him slipping them off this evening when he had come in and dropping them on to the table. He must have forgotten to take them to his room with him when he had gone to change. She went on staring at them, her eyes automatically going to the one that fitted the jeep.

Again she glanced behind her. The corridor was still empty and she hastily began to prise the key loose from the ring. Here was a chance to escape, given to her on a silver plate! This last hour had shown her all too clearly the dangers of remaining here; had also shown her why her desire to leave had started to become less desirable.

The magnetic personality of the man who imprisoned her was slowly turning her from an independent-minded woman into a creature with no will of her own. Worse than that: a woman who wanted to submit to *his* will! The knowledge made her shiver with shame, and she almost tore the key from the ring, dropped the bunch back on the silver plate and raced up the stairs. In a couple of hours, when everyone had retired for the night, she would go to where the jeep was parked and make her escape.

In her room she packed her case, glad it was small and easy to manage, then donned trousers and a light sweater knowing it would be cold once she reached the *alto plano*. She tried not to think of driving up the narrow mountain road in the darkness; tried not to think that this was the first time she would be at the wheel of a jeep. She must think only of freedom.

She looked at her watch. It was nearly midnight. Normally Ramon did not go to bed until one o'clock. She bit her lip.

She was already used to thinking of him by his first name and knew that only luck had prevented her from calling him by it. Yes, it was time she left this house. If she stayed any longer her heart would always be a prisoner here. Afraid to follow where her thoughts were leading her, she set her case by the door and went to peer down into the patio.

It was a full moon, which would make her more visible while she was escaping but would also serve to light the road for her. Surely that was a good omen? She looked at her watch again.

Time ticked slowly by, moving more quickly as it drew nearer to her departure. At one-thirty she unlocked her door and, case in hand, tiptoed down the stairs. The house was in darkness but moonlight illuminated the hall and flung dark shadows upon the high stone walls. Her heart beat fast as she tiptoed across to the huge wooden door. It was locked for the night and she prayed that the bolts were well oiled and would not make a noise as she slid them back. Gingerly she began to do so. The heavy iron bar slid back easily and with a quiver of excitement she opened the front door and stepped outside.

The valley was bathed in moonlight and the tropical green leaves had become blacks of varying textures. The wide clearing in front of the *hacienda* was empty of any vehicle and her heart began to hammer beneath her ribs. If the Land Rover had been locked away for the night, she was lost.

Quickly she hurried round to the side of the house where several outhouses lay. Some were used for storing food, one housed the dynamo and a large one acted as the garage. She ran to this, her case banging against her legs, and let out a gasp of relief as she discovered the wooden doors to be unlocked. As quietly as she could she opened them wide.

The jeep stood in front of her, its engine facing the wall. It meant she had to reverse it out and the knowledge almost made her give up the idea of escaping. But she stifled her fear, dumped her case in the back seat and clambered up behind the wheel. With the key in the ignition she hesitated. The noise of the engine was bound to be heard and Ramon would immediately guess what was happening and race down here. How long would it take him? Two minutes, possibly less. That would just about give her time to back out the jeep, turn it round and head for the road.

Encouraged by this conclusion, she turned the key. The engine roared in the silence of the night, drowning the frantic beating of her heart. Putting the gear into reverse, she went to release the brake. The lever refused to move and she pushed it down hard. It still remained locked and she pushed harder. Again nothing happened, and she lifted her foot from the accelerator and swivelled in her seat in order to place both hands on the brake. Unless she could release it she would never be able to get out.

How long was it since she had switched on the engine? Half a minute? Three-quarters? If she didn't hurry, she would be caught. Drawing a deep breath, she pushed at the lever with all her strength, almost sobbing with frustration. Slowly the lever inched down, not as low as she had expected, but sufficiently low for her to hope she had released it. Still concentrating on it, she put one hand on the wheel to swing it round. Her fingers curled over the rim and touched something that moved, and with a scream she wrenched her hand back and swung round to see what she had touched.

It was a hand.

Instantly her eyes shot upwards to meet the glittering black ones of Ramon de la Rivas.

'You!' she choked.

'Regrettably for you,' he replied, and reaching across her, whipped the key out of the ignition.

'I hope you haven't damaged the brake,' he continued.

'I couldn't get it to move.'

'Because I locked it.'

'You *what*?'

'I locked it. A few minutes ago. When I saw you leave the house.'

'You *saw* me?' she breathed.

'Yes. I found it difficult to sleep and went down to the library for a book. I was returning to my room when I saw you by the front door. I guessed what you were trying to do and I cut across the patio to here. I have a lock attachment on the brake which I use when I leave the car in one of the villages—it stops the children from accidentally releasing it. It has also, I am glad to say, stopped *you* from leaving here.'

'I suppose you think you're very clever,' she choked. 'But you can't keep me here for ever.'

'That has never been my intention.' He suddenly seemed to lose patience with her. 'I never thought you would abuse my hospitality in such a way.'

'Hospitality!' she stormed. 'You keep me a prisoner in this wilderness and you call it hospitality! You're out of your mind! I want to be free of you,' she cried. 'Can't you understand that?'

'You have the freedom of my house and you are treated as a guest. You had no right to abuse my trust.'

'And you've got no right to keep me here against my will. I hate you for it!'

'I didn't get that impression when we were in the *sala* tonight.'

'Because I wanted to get you off your guard; to make you think I was staying here willingly.'

'So you were pretending to like me?' He made no effort to hide his anger. 'Well, let's see how much of a pretence it was.'

Catching her by the shoulders, he pulled her down from the jeep. She stumbled and would have fallen had he not tightened his grip, bringing her body up against his hard, muscular one.

'Pretence, was it?' he repeated thickly, and pressed his mouth savagely upon hers.

For an instant she was passive, then she fought him: kicking, scratching, trying to bite. Her efforts enraged him and he pushed her hard against the car. The wheels dug into the back of her legs, making it impossible for her to go on kicking him. Her hands were powerless too, for he had caught them in his, at the same time leaning his body on hers to prevent her wriggling away from him.

'You won't escape me again,' he grated. 'You're my prisoner and you'll stay here until I decide you can go.'

'You're mad!' she gasped.

'You've driven me so. For days I've wanted to hold you like this; to taste the sweetness of your mouth, feel the warmth of your body.'

'Never!' she cried, and made a valiant effort to push him away.

'You can't escape me now,' he continued. 'I treated you with respect and you flung it back in my face.'

'I didn't! I only tried to escape. You can't blame me for that.'

'I blame you for pretending we were friends—for making me think we could be something more.'

'We *could* be something more,' she cried, seeing hope for herself in his words. 'But not while you force me to stay here. If you'd let me go I'd——'

'No more lies!' he cut in furiously. 'I won't let you fool me again. From now on *I* decide how we act.'

Roughly he tilted her chin and covered her mouth with his own. She felt the salt taste of blood, but she was unable to cry out. All she could do was to give a muffled groan and hope he would release her. But if anything, his hold grew tighter, though the hard pressure of his lips eased as he raised his lips slightly from hers and spoke.

'Kiss me back, Vanessa. Then I will let you go.'

'No!'

'You will.'

'Never,' she repeated. 'You can't make me.'

It was a foolish threat and she knew it the instant she heard his soft laugh. Releasing her hands, he placed both of his own around her shoulders. Wildly she hit out at his back, but he ignored it and began to rub the side of her neck with his tongue, at the same time moving his hands up inside her sweater. She tried to wrench away, but the writhing of her body only made him more conscious of her, and she felt the surge of movement that swelled his limbs.

'How soft your skin is,' he whispered as his fingers undid her lacy brassiere and curved around the fullness of her breasts.

His touch was soft as a flame on paper, but like a flame it devoured her and she shivered with desire, inhibitions burning away as his hands moved lower. Where before her lips had parted in pain, they now parted in passion, and the truth she had been unwilling to admit beat in her head like a thousand drums.

She loved him. She loved this wild, tempestuous man. Loved him for the way he cared about his people; the way he looked; the way he spoke. Loved everything about him.

It was a shattering admission and brought fear instead of joy. How could she love a man who kept her his prisoner and refused to take her word that she was not Delphine's partner? But logic had nothing to do with emotion, and where Ramon de la Rivas was concerned, she was *all* emotion. With a soft moan she relaxed against him. There was no point fighting him. She wanted him with every tingling nerve in her body, every year of her womanhood.

Sensing her change of mood, he eased slightly away from her and let his mouth travel gently down her slender throat. Pushing her sweater aside, he rested his lips in the hollow between her breasts, then he began to tremble violently.

'I want you,' he murmured against her skin. 'I knew it would be like this . . . I knew it.'

His hands continued to stroke her into pulsating life. Her stomach muscles contracted and deep inside her was an ache that only his possession of her could ease. But she dared not let this happen. Surrender would bring fulfilment, but it would also bring shame. And shame would outlast any other emotion he aroused in her.

Tensing her arms, she pushed at him with all her strength. Because he was not expecting her attack he had no defence against it, and he staggered back sharply. Before he had a chance to recover, she was free of him and running out into the night.

'Vanessa, come back!' His voice rang out. 'Come back!'

Heedless of his call, she went on running, trying to ignore the fact that he was coming after her. She increased speed, but knew he was getting closer, his shadow looming ahead of her, stark black in the moonlight. She swerved wildly to dodge him, but her foot caught on a stone and she sprawled heavily to the ground.

Crying with frustration, she was only half aware of him lifting her up into his arms. She was beyond caring what he did with her. If he took her here and now there was nothing she could do about it; nothing she would *want* to do. She loved him and could no longer go on fighting him. Sobbing with hurt and mortification, she turned her face into his shoulder. He cradled her as if she were a child, and she felt the swift pounding of his heart as he strode across to a side door and entered the patio.

Not until they reached the inner hall of the house did he set her down, still retaining a hold on her as she swayed. Only then did she get a proper look at him. His shirt was torn and there was a weal on his face where she had clawed him. A trickle of blood had dried on his cheek and he looked as if he had fought a duel and lost. Except that he had won. She drew a shuddering breath and pushed her tumbled hair away from her face. The lift of her arm made her realise her brassiere was undone, and her face flamed red.

'Go to your room,' he said quietly. 'We will talk in the morning.'

'We have nothing to say.' Her voice was almost inaudible, but he heard it.

'We have a great deal to say,' he replied. 'But you're in no state to listen. But one thing I *will* tell you. You will remain here until you've finished the tasks I have set you. Until then you would be wise to regard my home as yours, and stop seeing it as a prison.' His head lowered to hers, then he drew back sharply. 'Go to bed, Vanessa, while I still have the strength of mind to send you there alone.'

Turning, she fled from him.

CHAPTER EIGHT

VANESSA knew there was no way she could avoid Ramon the next day, and since it was her nature to face something she did not like, rather than put it off, she was downstairs before eight the next morning.

It was a particularly sultry day, with clouds low in the sky and the air as heavy as her mood. She had taken extra care with her appearance, wanting to remind herself that it was her beauty which had made Ramon kiss her with such raw passion, and not the more tender emotions of love. He was a man living in isolated splendour, miles away from his own kind of society. What more natural than for him to be inflamed by her proximity?

Leaves rustled behind her and she turned in the direction of the violet shadows on the far side of the patio. A darker shadow hovered there, then emerged and came forward. Her

pulse raced and then slowed to an erratic beat as Ramon de la
Rivas stopped in front of her.

'Good morning, Vanessa. I hope you slept well?'

'I locked my door,' she replied, and had the pleasure of
seeing the blood seep into his face.

'I deserved that.'

The humility in his tone was repeated in his expression.
He looked as if he wanted to apologise but did not know how
to begin. Or maybe he could not bring himself to begin. But
no—he was going to do so, for he drew himself to his full
height and gave her a half bow.

'I am deeply ashamed of my behaviour last night. I have
never lost control of myself before.' His eyes met hers and the
flecks of yellow seemed to intensify. 'No, that isn't true. I
have lost my control before, but—but never with a lady.'

The picture this evoked in her mind seared her with such
jealousy that she longed to hit him. But luckily he was unaware of this and went on talking.

'Last night was a lapse that will never occur again. As long
as you remain in my home you will be safe. I give you my
word.'

Contempt blazed in her eyes. 'Once before you assured me
of the same thing, but after last night I'm afraid I don't give
it much credence!'

The muscles in his face contracted. 'I was angry,' he said
in a strained voice. 'I had hoped that in the last few days we
had established a relationship. When I discovered it was all
an act . . .'

There were two ways she could interpret what he was saying; one indicated hurt pride, while the other showed a
genuine sorrow that her friendship with him had been simu-
lated. Because she desperately wanted to believe the latter,
she forced herself to believe the former.

'As I told you last night,' she said, 'it's difficult for a
prisoner to feel friendship towards his jailor.'

'I wish——'

Whatever he wished was never uttered, for at that moment
a servant called and scurried across the courtyard, speaking
in a dialect to which his master responded by moving swiftly
in the direction of the hall.

'Forgive me,' he called over his shoulder to Vanessa, 'but

some unexpected guests have arrived.'

She was startled by the news. The *hacienda* was hardly the place where people could drop in when the fancy took them, and she wondered what kind of visitors they were, who would arrive without notice. She perched on a wrought iron chair and stared at her hands. They were completely healed and she knew that today Josefina would be able to show her how to use the loom which had already been set up in place of the spinning wheel. She had done a little weaving at college and at one time had toyed with the idea of buying a loom of her own. But once she had started working for Delphine she had been too busy designing and making clothes to have any energy left over to make the fabric as well.

Restlessly she glanced at the house. Ramon should have met his guests by now and taken them to the *sala*, which meant it was safe for her to go in search of Josefina. Wryly she wondered how he would introduce her to his guests, or if he would introduce her at all. If they were only staying to lunch he might ask her to remain in her room.

The Indian woman was already weaving when Vanessa joined her, and she watched for some time before she felt sufficiently confident to take over.

To begin with she was slow, but soon she got the hang of it, and a couple of hours later had completed several inches. Although she had tried to follow Josefina's pattern, her own looked subtly different. Without realising it she had softened the angles of the Aztec design, giving it a more fluid look. She thought it an improvement and felt there were other variations she could do that would look even better. She set to work again and was soon so engrossed that she lost track of the hours.

Voices behind her made her swing round with a start, and she turned to see Ramon de la Rivas and another man and woman. They were obviously father and daughter, for they had the same small features and dark colouring, though where the man was rotund, the girl was roundly curved. Her face was the pure oval found in Greek sculpture but rarely in real life, and her black hair, parted in the centre and coiled in a thick chignon on the nape of her neck, followed the same classical mould. She wore only a hint of make-up on her olive skin, though mascara was lavishly applied to the thick lashes that framed dark, almond-shaped eyes. Her pink linen dress matched the colour in her smooth cheeks and was echoed on her lips and nails. No casual visitor here, Vanessa decided, but a beautiful girl dressed to beautiful advantage. Her eyes met the dark ones and it was easy to guess the thoughts behind them. She glanced at Ramon and wondered if he was aware of it too.

'Vanessa,' Ramon said quietly, 'I would like you to meet some friends of mine, Señor Oscar Moyas and his daughter Francisca. They are staying here for a few days.' He glanced at the couple. 'Miss Wayne came to Peru to study our traditional garments, and a mutual friend of ours in London suggested she contact me. I was lucky enough to be able to arrange for the wife of one of my workers to show her how we weave our materials.'

Oscar Moyas smiled at Vanessa. 'I'm delighted to meet someone who's interested in our traditional methods. Most young designers think only in terms of mass production. Do you travel to other countries too?'

'At the moment I'm concentrating on Peru,' Vanessa replied, marvelling at the ingenious way the younger man had extricated himself from an embarrassing situation.

'Vanessa owns a boutique in London,' Ramon intervened smoothly. 'She has had such success selling Peruvian clothes that she decided to come here and learn how they are made.'

'And after you have learned, Miss Wayne,' Francisca Moyas came into the conversation with husky delicacy, 'will you then make up similar clothes yourself and no longer buy from us?'

It was an intelligent question and Vanessa acknowledged it as such. 'I could never give them the authenticity my customers require. An imitation can be excellent, but it always remains an imitation.'

The girl nodded and moved gracefully over to the loom. 'Did you weave all this yourself?'

'This section only.' Vanessa pointed to it. 'I'm afraid it isn't the same as the original design I was shown.'

'But it's an interesting variation. Come and look at it, Ramon.'

'What does Ramon know of such things?' Oscar Moyas protested.

'He has an excellent eye for clothes, Papa.'

'You flatter me,' her host said with a smile, and obligingly stepped over to look at the design Vanessa had woven. His lower lip jutted forward as he studied it, and one long finger came out to trace the colours, as if trying to see the difference between her design and Josefina's. 'I agree with Francisca,' he said. 'There is a slight difference between the two, but it is very pleasing.'

Francisca linked her arm through Ramon's and he smiled down at her. 'Come, *chica*, I will show you and your father to your rooms. You must be tired after your journey and in need of a rest before lunch.' His glance went to Vanessa. 'I suggest you do the same. You have worked hard all the morning.'

'The weaving kept pace with my thoughts, *señor*.'

His lids lowered momentarily, but when they lifted again his eyes were focused on his guests and, smiling at them, he escorted them out.

In her own bedroom, Vanessa made herself tidy and wondered when it would be safe to go to the kitchen and ask for a tray to be sent to her room. It was preferable to lunching with strangers and having to simulate friendship with a man she loved yet despised. Despairingly she shook her head. What she felt for Ramon couldn't be love. It was physical attraction, nothing more, and it would disappear the moment he was out of her life.

There was a soft tap on the door, and even as she called 'Come in,' he appeared on the threshold. She caught her breath. Had she reached the stage when she could summon him to her by thought alone?

'Forgive me for intruding,' he said, coming in and closing the door, 'but I wish to talk to you.'

'If it's to ask me not to tell your guests that you're keeping me here against my will, then you needn't worry. They wouldn't believe me, anyway.'

'Indeed?' He looked puzzled.

'Have you forgotten what you said to me the first night I was here?' she asked crossly. 'That everyone would think I was your girl-friend and that if I tried to tell them the truth, they'd think I wanted to hurt you for cooling off me!'

Unexpectedly he smiled. 'As far as they are concerned, you needn't fear for your reputation. They know me too well to think I'd be indiscreet enough to introduce them to one of my—er—girl-friends.'

'Your concern for my good name surprises me!'

'It's my good name too,' he replied smoothly, then added: 'I take it I can trust to your discretion?'

'As much as I can trust yours.'

'Then we are both safe!' He opened the door for her. 'As we're supposed to have been introduced by a mutual friend, and you are here as my guest, it is more fitting that we use our first names.'

'As you wish.'

With a cool nod she walked beside him down the corridor. His nearness aroused an excitement in her that she could not control. It quivered through her body like a violin string too tightly strung, and she was afraid that if he came any nearer it would snap. And then what would she do? Throw herself into his arms and admit she loved him? Beg him to let her stay here for as long as he wanted her? The thought of losing her control was so unnerving that she stumbled.

'Are you feeling ill?' he asked.

'No, I . . .' She drew a deep breath. 'It's reaction from last night. My freedom was so close that I can't forget it.'

'It still isn't far away. You speak as if I'm never going to let you go.'

The idea appealed to her so much that she recoiled from it sharply and, misinterpreting the movement, his face hardened.

'I am as anxious for you to be gone as you are,' he said. 'But I intend to keep you here until you have done as I have ordered.'

'Or pay the prices you demand?'

'Exactly. If you wish to leave here so badly, all you need do is put your hand deeper into your pocket.'

'If it were *my* pocket I'd empty it in order to get away from you!' she flashed. 'But it isn't and I can't. Why won't you believe me?'

Before he could reply there was the closing of an upstairs door and the sound of steps.

'The Moyas are coming,' he said softly, and catching hold of Vanessa's forearm, pulled her after him.

He walked fast and she was out of breath when they reached

the *sala*. Ramon released her and rubbed his hand over his hair. It was as well groomed as always, and she wondered wryly if her argument with him had ruffled him so much that he felt ruffled outside too. It was a pleasurable thought and she concentrated on it, hoping she could hate him enough to exorcise the other emotions he aroused in her.

He crossed the room to stand by the huge stone fireplace, and a second later Oscar Moyas and his daughter came in. They had both changed, he into another light coloured tropical suit, and she into a white muslin dress. The softly flowing lines and the romantic style of her dark hair made her look like an Aubrey Beardsley drawing, though the smile with which she favoured her host had the provocation of a Toulouse-Lautrec.

Ramon greeted both of his visitors with equal warmth before he busied himself at the drinks tray, handing the man a whisky and Francisca a tall glass filled with pale green liquid.

'It is still your favourite, I hope?'

'My tastes do not change in six weeks.' Sparkling eyes toasted him over the rim of the glass.

Ramon acknowledged it and then raised his eyebrows at Vanessa.

'Nothing, thank you,' she said.

The smile left his face and he turned away abruptly to pour a drink for himself.

Oscar Moyas sat down beside Vanessa and began to chat. His English was heavily accented but fluent, and he knew London well, for he was in the export business and came there frequently.

'Ramon and I used to be competitors,' he informed her, 'but two years ago he suggested a merger and asked me to take over the day-to-day running of the company. He has so many other things to do that he is short of time.'

'Then why does he spend so much of it here?' she asked.

'Because his most important business is the welfare of the Indians in the Sierras.'

'It must be lucrative if he's willing to stay away from Lima.'

'It's only lucrative if one measures wealth by happiness,' Señor Moyas said dryly. 'From a monetary point of view, it brings him nothing. He has tried for years to bring industry to these areas and improve the standard of living, and he is just starting to succeed.'

It gave Vanessa a deep sense of pleasure to hear someone speak so highly of Ramon's efforts, and made her own refusal to pay the Indians more seem paltry in the extreme. Surreptitiously she eyed him. He was deep in conversation with Francisca, and there was an ease between them that told her they knew each other well. Turning back to the man beside her, she saw he was also watching the couple, and looking highly pleased with himself.

'My wife didn't want me to bring Francisca on this trip,' he said under his breath, 'but I'm glad I did. She was so anxious to see Ramon that I couldn't leave her behind.'

'Your daughter is very beautiful,' Vanessa murmured.

'She takes after her mother. My wife was only seventeen when Francisca was born, and still looks so young that the two of them are often taken for sisters. While I,' he chuckled, 'am often thought to be their father!'

'I don't believe that.'

'It's true. I'm fourteen years older than my wife. There's the same difference of age between Ramon and Francisca. She was nineteen last week.'

It was easy to see where Oscar Moyas' hopes lay, and Vanessa wondered if Ramon's hopes were the same.

At luncheon the two men talked business and Francisca, after listening for a little while, decided to satisfy her curiosity about Vanessa. She was obviously uneasy at the thought of another woman staying here, and Vanessa knew that an injudicious reply could quickly fan her jealousy. It was a temptation she knew she must resist, for if she didn't, Ramon might easily guess that her own jealousy had made her try to exacerbate Francisca's.

'How long are you staying here, Miss Wayne?' the Peruvian girl asked as the entrée dishes were removed and dessert plates were set before them.

'Not much longer. I have to return to England soon.'

'Will you be going back to Lima first?'

'Yes. My plane ticket's booked from there.'

The olive-skinned face relaxed: put at ease by the cheerful way Vanessa referred to her departure from Peru. And from Ramon.

'If you have the time, I'd be happy to take you to some shops that specialise in ethnic clothes,' Francisca offered.

'Vanessa couldn't pay their prices.'

Ramon came so incisively into the conversation that Vanessa knew he had been listening to it. Yet he had given the impression of being completely engrossed with Oscar Moyas. She could not help being amused. She had always believed that only the female of the species was capable of listening to two conversations at the same time!

'No shop can afford to buy from another shop,' she said calmly. 'They all like to go direct to the source.'

'It's easy to do that *here*,' Oscar Moyas informed her. 'But I'm sure Ramon has already told you that. And he can obtain the best prices for you, too.'

'I'm sure he can.'

As if anxious to take the conversation away from Vanessa, Francisca changed it to a topic in which she could take the limelight. Left to her own thoughts, Vanessa's eyes were drawn to Ramon.

He was listening attentively to his guests, his brows drawn together in concentration, his mouth relaxed but firm. The sunlight that filtered in through the windows cast a golden radiance over the smooth planes of his cheeks, throwing them into prominence and putting shadowy hollows at his temples. It was a face any sculptor would have been delighted to model, and the pleasure she derived from looking at him was so intense that she quickly averted her gaze. As she did, her eyes met Francisca's, and she knew that her appraisal of Ramon had not gone unnoticed. Hoping she had not given herself away, she concentrated on peeling a peach she did not want. The Peruvian girl—for all her tender years—was an astute creature, and even if she had guessed where Vanessa's emotions lay, would be too wily to tell Ramon. No female with intelligence would tell the man she loved that another woman desired him, for the man was not yet born who could remain unflattered by the knowledge. No; Francisca would say nothing.

Even so, Vanessa was glad when the luncheon came to an end and she could return to her weaving, leaving Ramon to take his guests on a tour of the valley.

She only ceased working at the loom when the light began

to fail, finding it too difficult to concentrate on her design in the lamplight. To pass the next hour she went into the library to see if she could find any books on Aztec art. She had never before come in here without Ramon, and she was aware of his presence in the very atmosphere of the room. The leather and suede chairs were the same rich brown as his hair and the gold-tooled books reminded her of the glints in his eyes.

Dismayed by the treachery of her thoughts, she pulled out the first book that came to hand. Luckily it was what she wanted: an illustrated volume of early Aztec carvings, and sitting at Ramon's desk she began to copy out some of the designs, altering them slightly as she did so.

By the time she had worked herself into a more tranquil state of mind, it was completely dark outside, and gathering her sketches she went to her room. She had to face dinner tonight and possibly several more meals with Francisca's watchful eyes upon her. It was an unnerving prospect and made her realise how strong her reaction was to Ramon. It was not only his physical attraction but his mental one that aroused her. Last night, when he had foiled her escape, she had managed to fight her feelings for him, but what would happen if he kissed her again? Would she still be able to control her response? More important still, would she want to?

Knowing the answer, she sank on to the dressing-table stool and tried to envisage her future if this happened. But there was no future for her with Ramon. He was an aristocrat who would choose the woman for his marriage bed as carefully as he chose the wine for his table. And one thing was sure: the future Señora de la Rivas would be as aristocratic and wealthy as her husband.

With a murmur of pain she rested her head in her hands. The emotion between Ramon and herself had nothing to do with love. It was a physical awareness that swamped everything else, and though strong enough to make him forget the future while he was living here, once he returned to Lima and his own friends she would be forgotten too. It was a girl like Francisca who would bear his ring, his name and his children.

CHAPTER NINE

VANESSA was the last to enter the *sala*, her reluctance to appear caused as much by fear as an unwillingness to wear a dress that Francisca might recognise as belonging to Ramon's sister.

Because of this she decided to put on the one dinner-dress she had brought with her, even though it was overly sophisticated for jungle dining! The black silk jersey was cut on severe lines and relied on the shape of the body inside it to give it contour; which Vanessa's body indisputably did. The sombreness of the material enhanced the creaminess of her skin, while her turbulent frame of mind was reflected in the intensified blue of her eyes. The glow of the gilded oil lamps turned stray tendrils of her hair to red, a colour that went well with her mood. Tonight she was like a tigress; claws sheathed but their presence felt.

Admiration was blatant in Oscar Moyas' eyes as they alighted on her, a fact which his daughter noted and disliked. Seeing the small white teeth nibbling the full lower lip, Vanessa realised that the girl was still sufficiently unsure of Ramon to be jealous of him. Yet would any woman ever be sure of him? Wouldn't she always fear that his virility and strong personality would attract the most beautiful girls to his side?

Though Vanessa refused to look at him directly, she was vibrantly aware of his tall figure by the fireplace, his white dinner jacket thrown into relief by the scarlet poinsettias that glowed behind him in the grate like flowery coals.

'I've poured you some champagne,' he said, not giving her a chance to refuse any, and came across with a brimming glass. His broad shoulders hid the two people behind him and, knowing it, he said softly: 'This is the first time I have seen you in black. You should wear it more often. It makes you look fragile.'

'I am, *señor*.' She half lifted the edge of her necklace to show the purple bruise left by his thumb the previous night.

He drew a sharp breath. 'Did I—do that?'

'And more besides.' Resolutely she met his eyes, triumphant when his were the first to drop.

'You have my *permiso* to do the same to me,' he said huskily.

'It wouldn't give me the same pleasure.'

A flush darkened his cheeks. 'You think I enjoyed hurting you?'

'Don't tell me you don't know your own strength?' she taunted.

'With you I have no strength.'

She knew exactly what he meant. How could she not when her own strength weakened so disastrously when he was near her? The glass in her hand shook and champagne splashed on to her fingers. Instantly he took a handkerchief from his breast pocket and carefully dabbed them.

'You are beautiful, Vanessa,' he whispered. 'Like a dark angel.'

She shivered, though not with fear. If he did this to her when he was only speaking to her, what chance did she have against him when they were alone and he took her in his arms? She knew he would forget the promise he had made not to touch her; not because he wanted to break his word but because he would not be able to stop himself. As she would not be able to help *herself*. Panic rose high. She had to leave the *hacienda*. If she didn't, she was lost.

Moving quickly away from him, she went to sit beside Oscar Moyas. 'Did you enjoy your afternoon, *señor*?' she asked.

'Very much. Ramon's work here is by way of being an experiment, and it is always interesting when one is—how do you say?—in on something from the beginning.'

'An experiment?'

'Has he not told you?' The man smiled. 'Ramon is always too modest to speak of his achievements.'

Since 'modest' was the last word she would apply to the lordly master of the *hacienda*, Vanessa said nothing.

'For a long while no one in the Government believed that his ideas would work,' Oscar Moyas continued. 'But he kept pressing them until they finally agreed to match his money.'

'Match it?' she queried.

'To put up the same amount he did. It was a vast sum, you understand. Larger for Ramon than for a Government department; and all of us—his friends and family—were anxious about the outcome. But as you can see for yourself, it is a great success.'

'What is?' Somehow she was sure Señor Moyas was not referring to the way Ramon was trying to get the Indian women more money for the garments they made. 'I'm afraid I don't know what Ramon's ideas were,' she added.

'They were more than ideas, *señorita*. They were his belief; his conviction. For years he has said that if the Indians in the high sierras were given modern farming equipment and had a centre to which they could send in their agricultural problems, they'd double their output and their living standards within five years.'

'And they have?'

'Without question. In three years Ramon has doubled the amount of land most Indian families are farming in this area. I still cannot understand how he did it.'

'The right machinery did it,' Ramon intervened, as always hearing all the conversation around him.

'It is more than that, my friend,' Señor Moyas said. 'Many others before you have tried to show the Indians how to use modern methods, but until you came along, no one had succeeded.'

'Because they lacked patience.'

'You underestimate yourself, Ramon.' Francisca favoured him with her standard look of adoration. 'You were the first to think of paying your farmers in goods instead of money. It was like putting handcuffs on them!'

Oscar Moyas chuckled, then seeing Vanessa's bewilderment, said: 'When the Indian has money in his pocket, he spends most of it on drink. That's why Ramon decided to pay them with equipment and goods for their homes.'

'But they still remain his tenants and workers,' she said. 'They're as dependent on him as their forefathers were on their Inca overlords!'

There was silence. Father and daughter looked at one another, but before the man could speak, Ramon did so.

'It is mainly the younger generation who wish to be free. The older ones prefer to have someone above them who will tell them what to do.'

'Only for the moment,' Vanessa argued. 'One day all the

Indians will want to live in the big towns. Life is easier there and they can get a decent education for their children.'

'There will always be people who prefer the life on the sierras to that of the cities.' Ramon sounded smugly sure. 'I have no fear of being without workers.'

'But, Ramon,' Francisca said impetuously, 'you are——'

'A cruel landlord who whips his people into submission!' Ramon finished for her, and gave Vanessa a smile that did not reach his eyes. 'We must be mindful how we talk to one another, Vanessa, or my friends will think we are enemies.'

Knowing herself beaten, Vanessa forced a smile to her lips and turned quickly to the older man. 'How long are you staying here, *señor*?'

'Not as long as my daughter would like. We are leaving tomorrow at daylight. We have an early plane to catch from Puno.'

Vanessa clenched her hands. Dare she say what she wanted or would Ramon prevent her? It was now or never and she had to take the chance.

'I wonder if you can give me a lift?' she said casually. 'It would save Ramon the trouble of taking me there himself.'

'It's no trouble.' Ramon intervened before the older man could reply. 'I have to go to Puno in two days' time and you've promised to stay here until then.'

'I would rather go tomorrow.' She challenged him directly, defying him to give himself away in front of his friends. But she had reckoned without his agile mind.

'Josefina will be bringing more samples of her work to the house tomorrow afternoon, my dear. She would be upset if you left without seeing them.'

Oscar Moyas chuckled, patting her arm. 'You are trapped. You cannot say no to Ramon now.'

'I certainly can't,' Vanessa thought mutinously, and beneath the sweetness of the smile she gave Ramon lurked venom that he saw and responded to by a hard, glittering look.

But if the conversation had fooled Oscar Moyas it did not fool his daughter. Senses heightened by love, she gave herself away when she came to stand beside Vanessa at the window, after dinner was over.

'If you want to leave the *hacienda*, Miss Wayne,' she murmured, 'do not let Ramon play on your good nature. I am sure Josefina will recover from any disappointment she might feel at your departure.'

'Ramon won't allow me to go,' Vanessa said bluntly, and then coloured with embarrassment. 'That isn't because we're . . . I mean, he isn't——'

'Please don't try to explain,' Francisca said swiftly. 'Ramon's affairs are too numerous for me not to be aware of them. But it doesn't stop me loving him,' she added, 'and I know that when we're married, he will be faithful to me. My way of life doesn't permit me the same freedom as the women in your country, but——'

'Please don't say any more,' Vanessa begged. 'You're quite wrong about Ramon and myself.'

'Then we will not discuss it.' The almond eyes were veiled by long lashes. 'My offer to help you remains. If you wish to leave the *hacienda*, I will take you.'

Vanessa stared through the window, seeing the Peruvian girl reflected in the glass, a fragile figure beside her own curvaceous one. 'Won't you mind that Ramon will be angry with you when he finds out you helped me to leave?'

'No. You see he . . .' There was a pause, as if Francisca was shy to continue. Then she spoke again, her voice stronger though still not loud. 'Ramon has now decided I am old enough to be married. Until now he has always said I was too young to know my own mind. But for the past two years I have looked at no one else, thought of no one except him— and at last, seeing and talking to me again, he has accepted that I know my own mind and will not change.' She moved closer to Vanessa, pathetically anxious. 'So you see, he will soon have no need of—of other women. N-nor will he want any.' Her lips trembled. 'I am very young, but I love him so much that I *know* I will satisfy him. I know it.'

'I'm sure you will,' Vanessa said huskily, then drew a deep breath. 'How can you help me get away?'

'Our car is left unlocked and you can hide under a blanket in the back seat. But get there early in the morning before the household is awake. I'll make sure our luggage is put into the boot, so you will be quite safe. We're leaving at six o'clock and Ramon won't think it strange if you say goodbye to us to-night.'

'You've thought it all out, haven't you?'

'You are at liberty to refuse,' Francisca said with pride.

'I wouldn't dream of refusing. But it all sounds so simple that I'm scared there's a flaw in it.'

'The earlier you get to the car, the better,' Francisca said. 'The waiting will be uncomfortable, but it is the only way.'

Vanessa nodded and turned back into the room, knowing it was unwise to be seen talking to Francisca for too long. As it was, Ramon was watching them and she deliberately sauntered over to a chair beside him, feeling like a mouse playing with a cat.

'The dinner was excellent tonight,' she commented. 'I find it hard to believe we're so far from civilisation.'

'The Incas were extremely civilised.'

'I wasn't thinking of it in those terms.'

'I know.' He was amused. 'But with a deep freezer and a dynamo, one can take the trappings of civilisation wherever one goes!'

'If you live like this here, I can't imagine how you live in Lima.'

'With slightly more luxury,' he said solemnly.

'A great deal more,' Francisca laughed, coming to join them and perching on the arm of his chair.

He put out a hand to steady her and Vanessa's stomach muscles tightened as she saw his fingers curl around the slender waist. Soon it would be the only one he would touch; her pretty red mouth the only lips he would feel. Looking into the delicate-featured face, Vanessa saw no depth of character. Could Francisca hold a man like Ramon for more than a few months? She doubted it, though the belief gave her no pleasure. What did it matter if he sought out other women, when she would never be one of them? Never, she repeated. It would be impossible for her to share the man she loved with anyone else.

'Such deep thoughts, Vanessa,' he remarked. 'May we share them, or are they private?'

With commendable quickness she found the answer to disarm him. 'I did some interesting drawings this afternoon. I'd like Josefina to weave a couple of them for me in different colours and in a much lighter weight wool. If the cloth is finer it can be made up into far more different styles.'

'That's an excellent idea.'

His mouth curved into a smile of pure pleasure. It lightened his face in a way she had not seen and she suddenly wished that what she had said was not a lie. Still, she had given him the idea and when she was gone he could tell Josefina. In fact she would talk to Delphine about it when she returned to London. London. It suddenly seemed like the Holy Grail. How wonderful it would be to return there and forget this brooding stone house and its autocratic master!

Because of their early departure in the morning, Señor Moyas excused himself shortly before eleven o'clock, though Francisca pouted prettily and said she had too many things to talk about with Ramon to consider going to bed so early.

'Don't keep her up too late, Ramon,' said Oscar Moyas.

'She will be in her room before the clock strikes twelve,' came the reply.

'That's the witching hour,' Francisca dimpled.

'So don't try to *be*witch me,' he grinned.

Vanessa, deciding her presence was *de trop*, rose too. Bidding father and daughter goodbye, and wishing them a pleasant journey to Puno, which she hoped would allay any fears in Ramon's mind, she went to her room. She tried not to think that she would never see Ramon again; that her last image of him was of his shiny dark head bent closely over Francisca's.

For the second time in a matter of days she packed her clothes, praying that this time there would be nothing to prevent her escape. She had forgotten to tell Francisca she was bringing a case with her and hoped the blanket in the car was large enough to cover both her and her luggage. If not, she would leave it behind; the main thing was to get away.

Her packing finished, she debated whether to go to bed. It was not yet midnight and though her instinct was to leave the house, she knew it was wiser to wait. The nights were cold and it would be uncomfortable crouching in the back of a car beneath a blanket. Yet she was scared to go to sleep for fear of not hearing her alarm clock, and she compromised by making herself comfortable in a chair with a coverlet wrapped around her.

She dozed fitfully and was wide awake by five o'clock and

longing for a hot drink. Contenting herself with some of the cold fruit juice that was always left in a thermos flask in her room at night, she tiptoed downstairs. Memory of the last time she had unbolted the front door—when she had not known that Ramon had seen her—made her look fearfully to right and left. The corridors were deserted and she opened the door, gently closed it behind her and raced to the Moyas' car, a sturdy station wagon.

A rough woollen blanket was thrown carelessly in the back and she quickly humped in her case and clambered in after it, drawing the blanket over her. It had a musty smell and was uncomfortably heavy, but she regarded it as a hair shirt and hoped that the penance of lying beneath it would absolve the guilt she felt at leaving in such a manner. Yet why should she care that she had lied to Ramon? If he had not behaved like a brute, she would have had no need to do so; would not have been here in the first place.

Time passed slowly. Her limbs grew cramped and every few minutes she shifted into another position. But there was little room to manoeuvre, for the front seats had been pushed back, leaving only a narrow space in which she could crouch.

The gradual warming of the air told her that dawn had given way to early morning, and this was soon proved by the increasing sounds of insects and birds. She pushed up the sleeves of her sweater and shifted her body yet again. Her feet were numb and the movement brought cramp in its wake, so that she had to bite her lip hard not to cry out. How much longer did she have to wait before the Moyas arrived? She tried to see what time it was, but the hands of her watch were too small.

In the distance she heard steps. Her heart thumped so loudly in her ears that she could not hear anything else. Then the steps came nearer and stopped, and she held her breath and waited to see if they moved on. But they remained by the car, walking first to the front and then stopping almost parallel with herself.

She hoped her head was not causing a bump in the blanket, but was scared to crouch lower in case the movement was seen. Her heart was racing so fast that one beat merged with another. She could not hear any conversation and knew it could not be the Moyas. Was it a servant with their luggage?

If so, why didn't he unlock the boot and put it in? The door nearest to her jerked open and she held her breath in case the rise and fall of her chest caused the blanket to tremble. There was no further movement and no other sound. Her scalp prickled with fear and she told herself nothing terrible could happen. There were no bandits here—only Ramon and his estate workers. Yes, that was who it was: an estate worker who had come to look at the car out of curiosity.

Her lungs were bursting and she expelled her breath as slowly as she could, hoping that whoever it was would close the door and go away. Suddenly there was a sharp intake of breath. The blanket was whipped away from her and Ramon's face, dark and furious, glared down into her own.

'So!' he hissed. 'I was right. Get out!'

Not waiting for her to obey him, he caught her arm and dragged her forward. Wedged between the back and front seat, and with legs numb from being bent double, Vanessa could not move to help herself, and she staggered from the car and fell to the ground.

'Get up!' he stormed.

She tried to obey, but her legs were incapable of moving, and with a muttered oath he bent and lifted her to her feet, gripping her viciously round the waist to keep her upright.

'You never learn, do you?' he said. 'I warned you what would happen next time you tried to escape.'

As he spoke he dragged her towards the house. Her legs were coming to life and pain was stabbing through them like a thousand needles. She tried to bend and rub them, but ruthlessly he pulled her into the hall and along the corridor to the room where she worked with Josefina. Pushing her into the centre, he threw her case in after her, stepped back into the corridor and slammed the door shut. The key turned in the lock and she flung herself against the panelling and beat her hands upon it.

'Let me go!' she cried. 'For God's sake, Ramon, let me go!'

In a frenzy of pain and anger she continued to beat on the door, and only when her hands were throbbing did she draw back and sink on to a chair.

What unhappy chance had brought Ramon down to the car? Had he known she was planning to escape with the Moyas? He had noticed her talking to Francisca last night, but she had never guessed he would realise what they were planning.

Jumping up again, she ran to the window. It was a narrow one, for the room did not face on to the courtyard and seemed to have been added to the house at a later date. She wondered whether to scream for help, but knew that even if the servants heard her they would not come to her aid. But what about the Moyas? Surely they wouldn't let her screams go unremarked? She began to shout, but her voice sounded flat, and she knew it was muted by the thick stone walls. Nevertheless she continued shouting, and only when her voice was hoarse and her throat aching did she concede defeat and lapse into silence.

She was crouched dejectedly on the chair when the lock turned and Ramon strode in.

'Come on,' he ordered roughly, 'we're leaving.'

'You're letting me go?'

In silence he picked up her case and disappeared down the corridor.

'Where are we going?' she asked, running after him.

Still he did not answer but strode outside to where the Land Rover was parked. Dumping her case in the back, he motioned her to climb into the front seat. As she did so, Josefina came scurrying round from the back of the house, the high-domed bowler on her head telling Vanessa she would be accompanying them.

Ramon took his place behind the wheel and they shot forward. Vanessa glanced at his profile, but it was so grim that she decided not to talk to him. Besides, she would soon know where they were going.

Making herself more comfortable, which was difficult to do when they were driving at such a pace, she huddled down and closed her eyes.

Inexorably they climbed and the valley dropped away below them, the tall trees gradually growing smaller until they resembled bushes, and the heat lessening until the coldness of the sierra took over. As the terrain became flatter their speed increased, and when an hour had gone by and she saw no sign of Puno, it dawned on her they were not heading in the direction of the town. With the passing of another hour this became a conviction, and looking carefully around her she realised they were heading for the mountain ranges that surrounded this flat basin of land.

'Where are you taking me?' she asked the man beside her, still not expecting an answer but determined to show some spirit.

'To a place I have in the mountains.' His voice was hard. 'You won't find it easy to escape from there.'

'What do you mean?' Fear made her forget her nervousness. 'I'm supposed to stay in your house and work with Josefina.'

'You will work with her in the mountains. It is the best solution.'

'Letting me go would be a better one.' She gripped his arm so hard that the jeep swerved. 'Let me go, Ramon! You've become obsessed with keeping me your prisoner.'

'You're the one who's obsessed.' He flung her hand away from his. 'If you had done as I asked, none of this would have happened. All I want is a decent price for the clothes my people make.'

'I can't do it!' Fury almost made for hysteria. 'It isn't *me* you have to convince—it's Delphine. If you think keeping me here will get you what you want, you're crazy! She'll never pay your price. She'll buy clothes from Chile or Bolivia.' Vanessa's anger rose to manic proportions. 'She'll go to Ecuador or Brazil. Yes, Brazil—that's where she'll go.'

'Our garments are unique,' he retorted. 'If they weren't, your partner wouldn't have come here twice nor sent you a third time.'

'She isn't my partner,' Vanessa enunciated each word and then clamped her lips shut. There was nothing she could say to convince this man that what he was doing was futile. The more she thought of it the more she realised that Delphine would never be blackmailed. Ramon's high-handed attitude would only make the woman more adamant in her refusal to comply with his wishes.

'We did excellent business before we sold Peruvian clothes,' she said in a tight voice. 'And Delphine will go back to French and Italian ones rather than let *you* dictate to her.'

Her only answer was such an increase of speed that she was shaken like a pea in a drum. Her bones were aching by the time they began to climb a narrow road that wound itself like a rope around a volcanic mountain ridge. The air became progressively colder the higher they went, and so did the wind. Vanessa's teeth were chattering and she motioned Josefina to open her case and take out her woollen jacket. Even wearing it she still shivered, and she pulled the collar high and dug her hands into the pockets.

On her left—so close that she could almost have touched it —the side of the mountain rose sheer, like a wall, while on her right it dropped sharply away. One false turn of the wheel and they would plunge thousands of feet to their death.

It was a terrifying thought and she huddled against the door and prayed that Ramon's temper would not make him careless. Why did he see her desire to escape as a personal affront rather than the normal reaction of a young woman who was unused to being kept anywhere against her will?

'P-please, Ramon.' She turned to him again, eyes wet with tears. 'Take me to Puno and let's end this farce. I've already told you I'll talk to Madame Delphine the moment I see her. If you like, I'll ask her to telephone you as soon as she's back from her convalescence.'

He didn't reply and, staring at his harsh expression, she knew she should have saved her breath.

A further hour of hairpin bends brought them to a small plateau and a village. It was so different from the one in the valley that it could have been on another planet. A dozen or so huts made up the small settlement, though her eyes rested in astonishment on a tiny stone church. Several Indians came out of their homes when they heard the sound of the jeep, and though there were no smiles of greeting—Indians rarely smiled—they raised their hands in welcome; a sign which Ramon returned, though he did not slow down until they had gone a hundred yards past the village to where a stone house clung to the side of the steep wall of rock.

Stiffly Vanessa clambered to the ground and went to help Josefina. But for all her age, the woman was down ahead of her and, carrying the cases, scurried forward into the house.

The whole of it would have fitted into the *sala* of the *hacienda*. It was also extremely primitive, with simple furniture, no water, and a paraffin stove for cooking. It was bitterly cold, and Ramon said something to Josefina, who immediately set a match to the black mounds in the stone hearth. It was slow to burn but gave off a good heat, though

Vanessa was given no chance to warm her icy hands at it, for Ramon curtly told her to take her case into the bedroom. There were only two, both no bigger than her bathroom had been, and each holding a narrow bed and a small table on which stood an oil lamp and a pitcher and bowl for water. Here was no hunting lodge, as she had imagined, but somewhere for a man to spend the night if he were caught in a storm and could not drive back down the mountain road to the plainlands.

She opened her case and donned another heavy sweater. It was pointless to unpack the rest of her things, for she had nowhere to hang them. She returned to the living room. It was empty, and she made a tour of exploration. There were four rooms in all—the two bedrooms, this central living room and a minute kitchen with a paraffin stove and the simplest of crockery and cutlery. There was also, she was relieved to see, an indoor lavatory with a chemical toilet.

Hearing sounds in the living room, she quickly returned to it. Ramon was warming his hands by the fire. For the first time that day she took in his appearance and saw he was wearing thick, cavalry twill trousers and a ribbed black sweater. It made him look like a demon and went well with his expression as he surveyed her.

'You'll have to cook and keep this place clean,' he said, 'as well as finish the weaving and make a poncho and a dress.'

'What do I weave with?' she asked, and followed his gaze to a small loom in the corner. Alongside it stood a bundle of wool in assorted shades. 'You can't expect me to weave all that,' she gasped. 'I'll be here for weeks!'

'Weave as much as you need to make the two garments. How long you stay here depends on how nimble your fingers are.'

'Can't Josefina——'

'She's here as a chaperone,' he cut in. 'She will do nothing to help you.'

Vanessa gaped at him. 'You can't mean that?'

'I do. Every word. So save your tears for someone who might be affected by them. The days are gone when you can get round me with your play-acting.'

CHAPTER TEN

VANESSA'S first week in the stone hut perched high on the volcanic ranges of the Cordillera remained ever afterwards as the nadir of her life. So harsh were the living conditions that for the first few days she was emotionally numb which, she realised afterwards, was Nature's way of helping her cope with a situation she would otherwise have found intolerable.

No one had ever treated her as unfeelingly as Ramon de la Rivas, nor shown such little understanding for the fact that, unlike the Indian women around her, she had not been brought up to withstand such primitive conditions and bleak weather. But from deep within her came a stoic determination not to give in which, she suspected, was what he was waiting for her to do. She had no means of knowing how he would have reacted had she done so, but his savagery towards her forced her to believe he had no spark of kindness in him whatever.

Obeying his instructions, Josefina did not help Vanessa and, on the one occasion when she had done so and had brought water from the reservoir in the village, she had been harshly reprimanded by her master.

As a child, Vanessa had been a Girl Guide for a couple of years, and she found herself utilising long-forgotten knowledge. After some initial difficulty she could manage to light a fire using a few scraps of wood—which were as precious in this treeless region as gold—and then kept it perpetually going by stacking dung cakes around it until they smouldered and began to give off heat and a sweetish but not unpleasant smell that bore no relation to their origin.

Carrying water was the hardest job of all. Each day she had to fill the small tank in the kitchen, for it was from here that the daily needs of the household were met. And how large those needs were! Drinking and cooking took up several gallons, as did their ablutions, the latter task being a twice daily penance, for it was always so cold that in order to wash with any degree of comfort one either had to do it by the fire in the living room—which meant everyone else having to go out—or in the privacy of one's bedroom, uncovering limb by shivering limb.

Two or three times each day Vanessa picked her way down the rocky road to the Indian settlement, watched by curious dark eyes as she went to the water reservoir. Quickly she filled her buckets and, carrying the yoke across her shoulders, laboriously retraced her steps up the steep road. The first journey was hard, the second harder and the third left her totally exhausted. But she had no time to rest; there was the food to prepare for lunch and, after the first two days, she found it easier to prepare the evening meal at the same time, when daylight seeped into the tiny kitchen and saved her working by the poor light of an ancient oil lamp.

Once the food was prepared, she swept the living room and her own bedroom—Ramon having curtly said he would do his own—while Josefina, who slept on a rug beside the fire, would unceremoniously bundle it up and tuck it away in a corner.

For the first few nights Vanessa would gladly have changed places with the old woman—the living room was at least warm—but then she found some extra blankets in a carved chest and subsequently managed to generate sufficient heat not to lie awake trembling with cold.

Though she rose with the dawn, by the time all the chores and preparations of meals had been completed it was after ten o'clock. Feeling she had done a good day's work, as indeed she had, she would settle in front of the loom and remain there until a grunt from Josefina told her it was time to heat up the food for lunch.

What a disaster her cooking had been initially! Despite a store of canned foods, she had to rely in the main on the dried goods stored in small sacks in a cupboard in the kitchen. There was maize, barley, dried salted meat and an odd assortment of herbs whose smell she did not recognise but whose flavour seemed to be uniformly hot.

She knew the maize and barley came from the terraced slopes a thousand feet below the settlement, and that many of the men went down to work there each day, while others tended the scraggy-looking llamas who somehow managed to find food amid the rocky outcrops of the landscape. It was an existence that bordered on starvation, and Vanessa marvelled that the Indians could work so hard on such a small intake of food. Either their metabolism was different from her own or else they had learned to disregard the cold and hunger which frequently threatened to sap her strength and always left her feeling half frozen and unable to think clearly.

Only in the living room did she find any degree of comfort, and she would sit by the loom, an oil lamp either side of her to give her light, and laboriously weave the cloth to make the dress Ramon had ordered. A pride she had not known she possessed in such prodigious quantity forced her to make an intricate design, and instead of keeping it only as a border, she wove it throughout the whole length.

There were different grades of wool in the huge bundle Josefina had brought with her, and she chose the finest skeins, re-aligning the loom to make a more loosely meshed material which was softer to the touch and would be more pliable to the scissors.

It was not until a week had elapsed that Vanessa had enough material for a dress, and with a sense of achievement she looked at the soft bundle in her arms and wondered how best to utilise it. The voluminous skirts favoured by the Indian women had been all the rage at the boutique, but she doubted if it was a lasting fashion and decided to work out a more classical style. She pondered on the idea of a Chanel type suit or a shirtwaister, then, because she was no copyist, discarded both ideas. She would create a dress suitable for the New World; something ageless, with a long graceful skirt and soft sleeves.

By the time she had worked out her measurements and the best way to get the maximum from the material, it was well past the hour to heat the supper. Folding the cloth into a neat bundle, she left it on her bed and went to the kitchen. To make the dress by hand would take at least three days of working non-stop. But since she also had the daily chores to do, it would take her double that time—possibly longer.

Without warning she was gripped by terror. She couldn't stay here any longer without going out of her mind. She put her hands to her temples and closed her eyes. It was not only the work that was sapping her strength but the close presence of Ramon. His proximity was turning her into a nervous wreck. She jumped whenever he came near her; felt her heart pound whenever he spoke to her: trembled like a feather in a gale when he looked at her. She was definitely insane. Why else should she love a man who was cruel and unbending; who would not listen to reason and who watched her suffering with hard, implacable eyes?

'I don't love him,' she muttered. 'It's desire, nothing more than that.'

Desire. She repeated the word silently, getting satisfaction in the shame of saying it. But it was better to feel desire than love; for love meant tenderness and understanding; compassion and companionship. And with Ramon she had none of these; only the naked urge to possess and be possessed.

A noise made her glance round and she saw him by the door. As always he wore dark clothes and they made him look exactly like the devil she knew him to be.

'I thought you'd be working,' he said.

'I've finished weaving the material.'

'Then start to make the dress. The sooner you get on with it, the sooner we can leave.'

Such a comment was more than she could bear, and words stormed out of her.

'Do you think I'd stop for even a second if I had the strength to continue? But I can't! My bones ache, my head aches and my hands are raw from the water and the cold.' She flung out her arms and pulled back the sleeves of her jersey so that he could see for himself. 'Look at them!' she stormed. 'If they get any worse I won't be able to do *anything*—and then what will happen? Will you lock me in a cell until they've healed, or will you come to your senses and let me go?'

He did not answer her questions, though his eyes narrowed as she thrust her hands directly at him.

'I'll put some cream on them before you go to bed tonight,' he said in a low voice.

'Will that absolve your conscience?' she cried.

'It's *your* conscience that concerns me. At least now you know how our Indian women live. But your life here is still easier than theirs. They don't have four rooms in which to spread themselves—usually two or three, with a brood of children who need to be taken care of as well.'

'Do you think I don't know that?' She was almost screaming with temper. 'I know how the Indians live and I'm sorry for them. But I'm not responsible for it. It's people like you—who've taken advantage of them for years—who should take the blame. You and your ancestors and all your stupid Governments!'

'Prepare the supper,' he said flatly, and retreated to the next room.

Eyes brimming with tears, Vanessa did so. In this last week she had lost weight, and there were hollows beneath her cheekbones and a milky pallor to her skin which made her hair look redder, as if all her vitality had gone into it. Her quarrel with Ramon had taken what was left of her strength, and she half-heartedly stirred the meat stew and added some of the frost-bitten vegetables which had appeared on the kitchen table that morning.

She was so long getting things ready that Josefina came in to see what was happening. Glancing furtively round to make sure her master was not there to see, she motioned Vanessa away from the stove and took the wooden spoon from her hand. She sniffed at the pot, gave a little cackle that showed toothless gums, then went to the store cupboard and took out a handful of assorted coloured pods which she dropped into the stew. Almost at once a piquant aroma filled the kitchen and Josefina went back to the cupboard and rummaged among the small sacks, adding to the cooking pot until it was filled to overflowing.

Vanessa sank on to a stool and watched the old woman. She could have hugged the bony shoulders in gratitude and, contrasting Josefina's behaviour with Ramon's, wondered that he had the audacity to consider himself civilised!

Half an hour later supper was set on the table. Josefina never ate with them but carried her bowl over to her corner by the fire, leaving Vanessa and Ramon to eat together.

'Your cooking is improving,' he said after the first mouthful.

She longed to tell him it was Josefina's handiwork but was afraid he would vent his anger on the old woman.

'I like the material you have woven,' he went on.

'You had no right to go into my bedroom!'

'I consider it safe for me to do so when you aren't there!'

'I'm the one to worry about safety, *señor*, not you.' Her

eyes sparkled with anger. 'Though you might have a hard time explaining to Señor Moyas why I'm staying *here* with you.'

Fork poised in the air, Ramon regarded her. 'You do not think he would believe the truth?'

'No one would.'

The broad shoulders moved in a characteristic shrug. 'Never mind. Oscar is a man of the world. And having seen you for himself . . .'

Vanessa longed to throw her plate into the sun-bronzed face, but was afraid her action would meet with the same one in return. If only she could hurt him as he was hurting her!

'And Francisca?' she demanded. 'Is she enough of a woman of the world not to object?'

'Despite her youth, Francisca's upbringing has taught her when to look away.'

'But have you no self-respect? Don't you care if she finds out?'

'Why should I?'

Vanessa flung him a look of contempt. 'Do you really need me to tell you?'

One curving dark brow elevated. 'Actually no,' he drawled. 'I'm well aware that Francisca likes everyone to know she is going to be my wife.'

Vanessa lowered her head and forced herself to pick up a forkful of meat. She dared not show the jealousy that raged through her. Ramon knew she was attracted to him—her wild response to his kisses had told him that—but he did not know how fierce that attraction was. Even to herself she was now determined not to use the word 'love'. She must denigrate her feelings for him; hold them in contempt in the hope that, once away from him, they would disappear.

'What do you think of Francisca?' he asked, for all the world as if they were having an ordinary social conversation about mutual friends.

'I don't know her well enough to pass an opinion.' Vanessa forced another mouthful of food into her mouth, hoping this would preclude further conversation. But Ramon was not to be put off.

'She is very beautiful, is she not?'

'Very.'

'Do you think she would make me a good wife?'

'I can't believe you're interested in my opinion, señor.'

With a great effort she raised her head and stared him fully in the face. During the eight days they had been here this was the first time they had had any lengthy conversation. Until now he had been content merely to say 'Good morning' and 'Good evening' to her, and to enquire politely as how her work was progressing, occasionally coming to stand behind her and watch her at the loom. Why was he now making conversation with her, and on such an intimate subject? Was he hoping to disarm her? To make her see him as someone with a beautiful bride in the offing—one she would not wish to harm by malicious gossip? Well might he be afraid, she thought mutinously, for when she returned to England she would lose no time in telling everyone what had happened to her.

Who did she mean by everyone? Newspaper reporters, or just Delphine and a couple of her own friends? And what would she say? That she had been held captive by a savage aristocrat in his hideout in the Andes?

Even if they believed such an unlikely story, would they believe she had been unable to escape? Any of her girl friends, seeing Ramon, would think her crazy for wanting to run away from him. A sigh escaped her. When she returned to London she knew she would do all she could to forget what had taken place here. Not only would she monitor her tongue, she would monitor her memories too.

'You still haven't answered my question.' Ramon's voice broke into her thoughts. 'Don't you think Francisca would make me an admirable wife?'

'The woman you marry would always make you an admirable wife, señor. You wouldn't allow her to do otherwise.'

In the lamplight his eyes gleamed like burning coals. 'If you mean I wouldn't marry a woman unless I knew she could give me what I want, then you are right. I have firm ideas as to what I require from marriage.'

'You don't say,' she said sarcastically, and saw the flash of his teeth as he smiled.

'You think it wrong to have everything cut and dried?' he enquired.

She hesitated, then said, 'Man proposes and God disposes.'

'That's true.' He set his fork down with a clatter. 'Unlike

so many people today, I don't take the marriage vows lightly. For me it will be a permanent contract, and because of it I must choose with care. Unless I was sure my marriage was going to be a perfect union between two people, I wouldn't enter into it.'

'How can one guarantee such a thing?' Vanessa asked, curiosity getting the better of her intentions not to converse with him.

'There are no guarantees,' he said after a pause. 'One can only do one's best and choose with deliberation.'

'But you can't love someone just because they're suitable,' she expostulated, and was amazed when he leaned back in his chair with a deep sigh.

'I thought I could.' His lids lowered and his eyes became black slits. 'It was a great shock to me when I discovered I couldn't control my heart. I believed the girl I loved was wrong for me. She did not think the way I did; did not understand my commitment to the Indians and—and many other things. Yet I still could not tear her out of my heart.' His lids lifted and his eyes were seen in their full darkness. 'Do you believe in a love like that, Vanessa? A love that's so strong it overpowers reason?'

Because she knew exactly what he meant, she determined to deny it. 'I don't believe you can love someone if you've nothing in common with them. What you're talking about is attraction, nothing more.'

'I thought so too, at one time,' he said abruptly, and rose from the chair, his tall frame making a long shadow over the walls, as she knew his memory would cast a shadow over the rest of her life.

'I felt that if I could hold her in my arms—take her—possess her—I would cease to want her.' He stopped abruptly, his teeth biting hard on his lower lip before he suddenly burst out: 'Does such plain speaking shock you?'

'No,' Vanessa said shakily, and tried not to hate the girl who could arouse such depth of feeling in this unfeeling man. He was certainly blinded by passion if he believed Francisca was his ideal woman. Yet a moment ago he had admitted she was not what he had hoped for, but that he wanted her just the same.

'Never marry someone believing you can change them,'

she continued. 'Because people don't change.'

'Being in love has started to change *me*.' His head lowered in reflective thought. 'I'm not the man I was.'

'Really?' She did not hide her scepticism.

'Really?' He echoed her word though not her inflection. 'I now realise that if I married someone who always thought the way I did, I'd soon be bored with her. A marriage can only be meaningful if there's an exchange of ideas; even to accept that on certain things one must agree to differ.'

'Then there's hope for you yet!' said Vanessa, and rose to clear away the dishes.

'Leave them,' he ordered. 'Josefina will do them tonight. It's unwise for you to put your hands in water.'

Reminding herself that his concern stemmed from guilt and not kindness, she nodded and sat down again, drawing her chair closer to the fire. Had it been warmer in her bedroom she would have gone there, but she was too on edge to sleep and did not fancy the prospect of lying wakeful in bed for hours. Behind her she heard Ramon prowl the room. There was the scrape of a match followed by the pungent smell of a cheroot. Forever afterwards she would associate this aroma with him, and she prayed for the strength to maintain her composure until they could separate and go their different ways.

'Will you be starting on the dress tomorrow?'

His voice was so close that she knew he had come to stand next to her. But she stared resolutely into the glowing fire.

'I'll start it as soon as I've finished the housework.'

'I'm not rushing you.'

'I can well believe it!' Only then did she swing round. 'You must enjoy watching me jump to your command.'

'No!' he said vehemently. 'I don't.'

One of his hands lifted as he spoke and she saw it was tightly clenched. She jumped to her feet, frightened by the turmoil on his face. The swiftness of her movement made her stumble towards the fire and he shot forward and pulled her back. His hands remained on her and he stared into her face. Her eyes, blue as cornflowers, were filled with defiance, but before she could read the expression in his, his mouth came down on hers, crushing it with an intensity that made her wince. Once before he had kissed her with the same savagery and then she had fought him like a wildcat, but tonight she stayed motionless, knowing the futility of fighting either him or herself.

'I love him,' she acknowledged. 'And if he wants me, he can have me.'

Fiercely his arms wrapped themselves around her, then one of them moved up to tear away the ribbon that confined her hair. As the dark tresses fell free he buried his face in them, then moved his lips along the side of her temple to her ear. His fingers were warm on the nape of her neck as he gently massaged it. She shivered and he drew her closer. Tremors ran the length of him and the swelling hardness of his body told her the effect she was having on him. Once again his mouth sought hers, but this time it moved softly over her lips, teasing them apart. Still she offered no resistance, neither turning her head away nor pushing her hands against his chest. It was as if the emotion she felt was not a part of her, as if she were in a dream, looking down upon herself.

Her stillness made him draw back.

'Forgive me, Vanessa.' His voice was barely audible. 'I don't want to take you like this. I want you to——'

'Resist you?' she cut in tonelessly. 'Do you want me to fight for my honour so that you can prove how strong you are? Well, I won't! I'm your prisoner and you can do as you like with me. But I'll never, *never* give you the satisfaction of fighting you!'

Her words were like a whip upon his skin and it reddened as he stepped away from her. 'Do you think I'm an animal, that I would take a woman in cold blood?'

'Not cold blood,' she sneered. 'Hot blood and lust! That's all you're capable of feeling. You locked me up in your house and when I tried to escape, you brought me here—where escape is impossible. So finish what you set out to do.' She moved close to him. 'Go on, Ramon, take me. Take me and then hate yourself!'

'I do already. If I . . . if . . .' He stumbled on the words and began again. 'I would never take you by force. You've got to believe that. I kissed you because I . . .'

He half turned away and she saw his profile, beautiful yet pagan, with its firm nose and chin and the thick black hair that swept up from a broad brow.

'Yes?' she questioned. 'You kissed me because of what?'

The look he gave her was so full of anguish that she was startled. 'I can't finish that sentence, Vanessa. I have no right to do so.'

Silently he left her and she huddled close to the fire. Words were not needed because she knew what he had wanted to say: that he was not free to tell her how he felt because he was betrothed to Francisca. At least he had the decency not to lie about it, though it was poor consolation to her at this moment

Ramon! She murmured his name soundlessly and thanked God that he did not know how easily he could have made her his. Yes, she still had her pride; though at this moment it was singularly poor consolation.

CHAPTER ELEVEN

RAMON must have told Josefina to do the household chores, for Vanessa awoke to find the fire lit, the small tank in the kitchen filled with water and breakfast prepared.

The meal was almost palatable—tinned sausages served with maize cakes—and she felt more replete than she had been for days as she collected the length of material from her room and started to work on the dress.

It gave her a deep sense of satisfaction to know she had woven the yarn herself, and for a while she kept it draped against her body and enjoyed a pride of ownership she had never felt when handling the expensive materials for which Delphine had paid a fortune. 'But I've paid for *this*,' she admitted bitterly, laying the material flat on the floor which Josefina had freshly scrubbed. 'Every yard of it has cost me my pride and peace of mind.'

Feeling as if she were cutting into herself, Vanessa picked up her scissors. Swiftly the pieces shaped themselves beneath her eyes. She had no paper pattern from which to work, but because she was making the dress to her own measurements there was less error involved. Nevertheless she worked with care, and it was lunchtime before all the pieces were cut.

Ramon did not appear and Vanessa looked enquiringly at Josefina, who padded away and returned with a sheet of paper covered with firm black writing.

'I have gone to Puno but expect to be back tomorrow afternoon,' he had penned. 'You will be safe with Josefina until my return. Forgive me for last night. Soon I hope it will not be necessary for me to ask your forgiveness again. Ramon.'

His last sentence was the one which Vanessa echoed wholeheartedly, knowing that her parting from him could not come soon enough. She folded the letter and put it into her handbag. In the years to come it would be her only reminder of this painful interlude.

As she worked on her dress, tacking the pieces together, Josefina took another needle and thread and started to help her. The two of them worked deftly and within a few hours the dress was tacked and ready to be tried on. There was only a small mirror available, but it showed Vanessa enough to tell her all was going well, and she drew off the garment with care, knowing that the work ahead would be far easier, although extremely tedious.

For the rest of the afternoon and evening they worked unceasingly. The skirt was wide and fluted, carefully cut in order to cling yet give fullness, and twice Vanessa had to undo the seams and re-stitch them before she was satisfied that they hung well. The bodice presented difficulties too, its very simplicity requiring careful sewing, and she decided to leave it until the following day when she would come to it with fresh eyes.

'You've been an enormous help, Josefina,' she said in slow Spanish, and though the woman did not understand all her words, the meaning must have been clear, for she cackled with pleasure and held the dress up for a moment before draping it carefully over a chair.

Vanessa went to her room, keeping the door into the living room open in order to get the warmth from the fire. Only now did she miss Ramon's presence and know a momentary fear at being among primitive Indians miles away from civilisation. It was a scaring thought and a movement from the next room made her gasp with fear. But it was only Josefina shuffling towards her with a cup and saucer in her hand. Unbelievingly she saw it was hot chocolate.

'Señor de la Rivas must have been hiding this tin,' she said with a slight smile, and Josefina grunted, the mention of her master's name making her eyes twinkle.

Vanessa sipped the drink with slow enjoyment. It was days since she had felt so warm and comfortable. Outside a bitter wind was howling, but inside the stone house it was snug. London seemed a million miles away and she had to force herself to think of Delphine. Was her employer still convalescing, or had she returned to the boutique? If so, she must surely be perturbed at not hearing from her assistant and would start to make enquiries about her through the British Embassy in Lima. Perhaps Ramon had gone to Puno to call at the hotel where she had been staying and see if there were any messages for her? He might even have the nerve to cable London and sign it with her own name. Still, if he did, it would at least stop Delphine worrying.

'How much longer will he keep me here?' She asked the question aloud and her voice brought Josefina in to look at her enquiringly.

'There's nothing wrong,' Vanessa said, and gave a smile to indicate the meaning of her words. 'Goodnight, sleep well,' she said in Spanish, and the phrase was simple enough for the old woman to understand.

The following day they continued to work on the dress, and by early afternoon it was ready to press. The iron Vanessa found was so rusty that she had to scrub it with a stone before she could use it, but she managed to iron the seams flat. The dress had turned out well and she was delighted. The loosely woven fabric was soft enough to drape and the rough wool had a mohair texture that gave it a cobweb delicacy. It was completely different from the normal run of Peruvian clothes, and she wondered if Josefina would be able to show her countrywomen how to weave in this particular way. If they did, they would find even wider fields for their work. Excitement stirred in her. How marvellous it would be to design a new range of garments instead of the ubiquitous poncho— which was limited in its use—or the voluminous skirts that were so unflattering unless one had the figure of a sylph. She thought of simple dresses with uncluttered lines; high-necked blouses with softly gathered skirts; elegant tunics and jackets. The scope was enormous, and with the right teaching the Indian women could combine the old skills with the new.

How delighted Ramon would be with her ideas! She had a strong suspicion he was counting on her being able to devise ways in which Peruvian clothes could be made more saleable in the West, and it would be playing into his hands if she gave them to him.

Moodily she went to the window. The skies were downcast and grey. Though the settlement was only a few hundred yards below her she felt as isolated as if she and Josefina were the only two people in the world. What would happen if Ramon didn't come back? Fear uncurled in the pit of her stomach. It was irrational, but she could not help it. Suppose he was taken ill or had an accident? How would she and Josefina get to Puno? Even by jeep it was hours away, and she doubted whether the Indians had any form of transport. Her fear grew so strong that she could not remain where she was, and slipping on her coat and tying a scarf around her head, she battled her way against the fierce wind down to the settlement.

No one was about. The men must have gone to the next village to work and the women were probably preparing food of looking after the children. She toyed with the idea of going into one of the houses, but knew that even if she did, she would not be able to make herself understood.

Ahead of her lay the little church and next to it huddled the priest's stone house. Ramon had told her the man only came here once a month, brought in the car by Manuel. Yet something drew her to it and she hastened her steps as she saw a curl of smoke wisping up from a hole in the steep roof. She knocked on the narrow wooden entrance and heard a voice raised in answer. Not sure if it was bidding her to enter, she pushed open the door and did so.

The hut consisted of one large room. The Peruvian bedsitter, she thought with some amusement, seeing a tiny paraffin stove and sink at one side and a narrow bed and table at the other while in the centre stood a small dining table and four chairs. A fire burned in the hearth and on the wall above it hung a large and resplendent cross. An Indian woman of indeterminate age looked enquiringly at Vanessa and shook her head. Vanessa realised the priest was not here, but when the woman gestured and pointed through the small aperture which served as a window, she gathered that he was expected to arrive from Puno.

Disappointed, Vanessa retraced her path up the narrow road to the lodge. Had she been able to talk to the priest he might have helped her to escape. But if he were coming today then he would be brought by Ramon himself, who was certain to make sure she had no chance of being alone with him.

Entering the warm living room, she was reminded of the poncho and fur-trimmed jacket she still had to make. It was another four days' work at least, and by the end of that time she would have been Ramon's prisoner for three weeks. By then Delphine would have organised a search for her and Ramon would be forced to set her free. But would anyone believe her if she said he had held her captive? The more she thought of it the more likely it seemed that everyone would think she had fallen captive to his charm and had stayed with him willingly.

'*Señorita, señorita!*'

Josefina's excited call told her what her own ears had failed to hear: the sound of a labouring engine as the Land Rover mounted the road to their hut and came to a stop. The car door slammed, the front door opened and Ramon stood there, tall, dark and unsmiling.

'If you had remained in the village a little while longer,' he said without any greeting, 'I could have given you a lift back.'

'I needed the walk.'

'Why did you go into Father Martin's house?'

'I saw smoke coming out of the chimney and thought he was there.'

'I brought him back with me.' Ramon's voice was still hard.

'It's odd to have a church for so few people,' she commented.

'Forty-five souls,' he replied, 'and sixty in the village further down.' He relaxed slightly, as if mollified by her interest. 'Father Martin invited us to have supper with him tonight. You will like him, I think. He's been offered many other positions, but he says the Indians here trust him and he would feel unhappy to leave them.'

'He sounds like a saint!' Vanessa replied. 'I can't imagine anyone staying here from choice. It's like hell on earth.'

Yet it was heaven when Ramon was near her. She turned

away from the thought, moving physically too, and found herself by the window. She pretended an interest in the view. Undulating mountain ridges stretched limitlessly to the horizon's edge. Somewhere far below stretched Lake Titicaca and beyond it lay Bolivia. The name had a magic sound to it, as did Peru itself, and both would forever be associated in her mind with the man standing close behind her.

'Has it really been hell for you here?' he asked.

'What do *you* think? I've been freezing, hungry, lonely and frightened.'

'Frightened?' The word was sharp. 'Of me?'

It would have been more truthful to have said of herself, but that would have given her away, and instead she nodded.

'Yes, of you. I've had the feeling you wanted to keep me here indefinitely.'

He stepped closer to her, forcing her to move and turn. She saw his face and noticed the frown that marked his forehead.

'Occasionally I've wanted to prolong your stay,' he admitted, 'but no matter how great the temptation, my code of honour would have made it impossible.'

'Three cheers for your honour,' she said with a flippancy she was nowhere near feeling. It brought a spark of anger to his eyes, as though he resented her humour; yet humour was her only defence against him.

'I've finished the dress,' she added the *non sequitur*, and went into the bedroom where she had draped it over a chair.

Ramon was close on her heels and motioned her to hold it up. 'Did you make it to fit yourself?' he asked.

'Yes.'

'I would like you to wear it tonight.'

It was a statement, not a request, and she guessed it would always be this way with him. He would never ask the woman in his life if she wished to do anything; he would take it for granted that what he himself wanted was her wish too. And he was probably right. Women, being the creatures they were —despite their hard-won independence—would fall over themselves to please him.

'What did you say?' he asked. 'You're muttering under your breath.'

'I was thinking what fools most women are when they're in love.'

'Men can be bigger fools. They lose their analytical capacity and are ruled entirely by their passion.'

Angrily she noticed that mention of love made him think only in terms of passion.

'You recognise the symptoms so well, *señor*, I can see you've often suffered from the disease.'

'And am still suffering!'

Behind them a pot clattered in the kitchen and she put the dress back over the chair. 'I think that's Josefina's way of saying lunch is ready.'

'Then you've been saved by the bell from hearing the rest of my confession. You might have found it interesting.' His smile was sharp.

'I doubt that. Love affairs make very tedious case histories.'

She walked out before Ramon had a chance to reply, and when he joined her at the table he made no reference to what they had been speaking about. Instead he was surprisingly communicative about his trip to Puno, telling her of the factory he had visited and the man he had seen.

'I thought you went down specifically to bring back Father Martin,' she commented.

'My main reason was to attend the Trade Fair at Puno. Usually they're held in the capital, but this year the Government was advised to hold it here. It's one way of making sure foreigners realise Peru doesn't begin and end with Lima!'

'An excellent idea,' she said.

'Thank you.'

His tone made his words clear and she regarded him with astonishment. 'You?'

'Why should that surprise you? Don't you know I want to encourage industry and commerce to move into *other* regions of my country?'

'I thought you were primarily interested in helping housebound Indian women.' He looked so perplexed that she was obliged to explain what she meant. 'If you can keep the wives content, it's one way of ensuring that their husbands remain with you.'

There was a long pause. His face darkened with anger, but when he spoke, his voice did not reflect it.

'You enjoy thinking the worst of me, don't you? That I only think of the welfare of others if it affects my own well-being?'

'It's what you've led me to believe,' she said stiffly.

'Do you think that *all* the men in this region work for me? I have a large *hacienda*, it's true, but it doesn't take in the entire Department of Puno!'

Put like that, it made Vanessa see she might have been sweeping in her judgment, and she was debating what to say when he spoke again.

'The welfare of *all* the Indians is my concern: the women as well as the men. If I have only spoken to you about a small section of them, it's because I didn't think you were interested in learning of the problems outside your own small industry.'

'The fashion industry is hardly small!'

He shrugged. 'Hand-made fashion is nothing compared with mass production. And that's where prosperity lies—catering for the masses.'

'You have set yourself an ambitious task, *señor*.'

'I am not driven by ambition,' he said crisply, 'but by anger at the poverty and hardship around me.'

'With such sweeping reforms in mind,' she retorted, 'I'm surprised you waste your time with one little boutique. You should be concentrating on overcoming the sales resistance of the chain stores.'

'First things first. We need to change our style—to make a move out of ethnic clothes into a proper Peruvian fashion industry.'

'I can already see Paris trembling!'

'Italy wasn't a serious contender until twenty years ago,' he said. 'But now as many buyers go there as do to France.'

'Italy's always been noted for its silk industry. It gave them the springboard they needed.'

'*Our* springboard is our massive labour force. *That* and our unique culture.'

Because Vanessa found the whole idea of what he was saying so exciting, she refused to be drawn into further discussion. She didn't want to catch his enthusiasm; nor be fired with the same motivation. His people were not hers and, unlike Ruth and Naomi, the parting of their ways was inevitable.

'When I was in Puno,' he said into the silence, 'I cabled your partner that you were well and busy and would be contacting her shortly.'

'And put my name to it, I suppose?'

'Naturally.'

'How clever you are!'

'Not clever enough.'

His mouth, always so mobile, moved as though he were in pain, and she wondered what thoughts could be causing it. Surely not regret? A man like Ramon would never doubt his own divinity!

'Aren't you curious to know what I mean?' he asked suddenly.

'I'm sure you'll tell me if you want me to know.'

This time his mouth showed wry appreciation of her sarcasm. 'If I were meeting you today for the first time, I would behave quite differently. I would ask you to stay with me as my guest and try to give you some understanding of the way we are tackling the problems of this region. Instead, I tried to force you to do as I wanted without making sure you understood my motivation.'

'I've always understood *that*!'

'No!' It was an angry reproach. 'I know what you mean and you're wrong. It wasn't until later—after I got to know you—that I . . .'

He was struggling not to speak and she waited tensely, wondering how honest he was going to be. But his discretion was too strong—or perhaps self-preservation was a better word—for he pushed aside his plate and reached into his pocket for a cheroot; a sure sign that he was retreating from the truth. The sweetish aroma of tobacco filled the room and Vanessa had to restrain herself from breathing in deeply. She mustn't allow his nearness to sway her mood. He was dangerous as a tiger and she must be constantly on her guard. Yet how she longed for him to hold her; to have him touch her with those long, narrow hands.

'There's no need for you to make any more garments,' he said abruptly. 'I'm sure you already appreciate how hard the women work.'

Blankly she stared at him. His matter-of-fact words were like a cold douche on her overheated emotions, and the abrupt transition from one mood to another made her feel physically sick. She swallowed, then closed her eyes for a few seconds and breathed deeply.

'You mean I can go?' she said slowly.

'We will leave here the day after tomorrow, when I take Father Martin back to Puno.'

'I don't want to have dinner with him,' she said abruptly, unable to face the prospect of making conversation with a stranger when all she wanted to do was lock herself in her room and cry.

'Why not?' Ramon asked.

Wildly she searched for a suitable lie. 'Because I don't want to dine with you socially. I eat with you here because I have no choice.'

A swift exhalation of smoke was the only visible sign of his anger.

'You have a cruel tongue, Vanessa. If I believed you meant that, I'd——'

'I do mean it!' she flung at him, and pushing back her chair rushed into her bedroom.

She expected him to come after her, and for several minutes waited, trembling, for him to do so. But when she heard his steps they carried him away from her, and she knew he had left the house. But she remained in her room for the rest of the afternoon. The closed door did not permit the warmth of the living room to seep through and she huddled under the blankets. Damn Ramon de la Rivas! No—not that. She did not want him damned. She loved him and even though he loved someone else she did not wish him to be unhappy.

The gloom of the afternoon gave way to the dusk of evening. She lit the oil lamp and thought of the battle ahead of her if she persisted in her refusal to have dinner with the priest. She was convinced Ramon would make her obey him, and rather than give him the pleasure of exerting his authority, decided to do as he wanted.

Shivering in the cold air, she slipped out of her trousers and thick sweater and put on the cream woollen dress that had cost her so much effort to make. Uncaringly she let her hair fall the way it wished, dispassionately noting that the loose waves framing her face enhanced the mediaeval look of the dress. In the small, misshapen mirror her eyes looked enormous, their blue intensely bright. Ramon had never remarked on their colour and she could count the compliments he had given her on the fingers of one hand. Yet she knew he wanted her; that he was fighting with himself not to take advantage of his superiority and her vulnerability. If only his desire for her had been gentled by love, how quickly she would have given in to him. Soured by the thought, she stormed into the next room and glared at him.

'I'm ready!'

'So I see.'

He rose from his chair by the fire. He had changed his dark sweater for a honey gold cashmere one. It was almost the same colour as his skin and it made him look like a sun-kissed god. Averting her eyes, Vanessa waited for him. From the corner of the room he picked up the white fur coat and held it out to her.

'Put this on or you'll get a cold.'

'So will you,' she said involuntarily, and he half smiled and reached for a fur-lined parka.

'A short while ago I had the impression you wouldn't care if I froze to death!'

'*After* you've taken me back to Puno,' she flashed, and marched out to the jeep.

CHAPTER TWELVE

IT was the first time Vanessa had been out at night in this altitude and she stopped as though hit by an unseen force. It was unbelievably, bitterly cold. It took one's breath away and made filling one's lungs with air a Herculean task.

'You will soon get accustomed to it,' said Ramon, guessing how she felt, and offered her his hand to help her into the jeep.

Ignoring it, as she always did, she took her place beside him and they began their tortuous descent. The drop on one side of them was horrific, but she was unafraid, knowing that wherever Ramon was, she would feel safe.

'We're nearly there,' he said, and she saw a glimmer of light coming from the stone hut beside the little church.

Father Martin was a surprise: a bone thin man with the face of an ascetic and the smile of a cherub. Yet according to Ramon he enjoyed the hardship of ministering to this far-flung, poverty-stricken community.

However, there was nothing poverty-stricken about the meal he set before them, and Vanessa was sure he had brought the food with him especially to entertain them.

'I don't normally eat as well as this,' Father Martin confirmed her opinion when, the lamb chops demolished and the dried fruit salad with its liqueur flavouring savoured to the last raisin, they returned to sit by the fireplace. 'But when Ramon accepted my invitation for tonight, I felt I had to do honour to his presence.'

'You flatter me, Father,' the younger man said.

'If you were a man who responded to flattery you would spend more time in Lima and less time here,' the priest replied. 'When I think of——'

'I like it here,' Ramon intervened, and then looked round for his box of cheroots. 'I must have left them in the jeep,' he muttered, and shrugging into his parka, went out.

Vanessa looked quickly at the priest, wondering what explanation Ramon had given for her living here with him.

'I gather you've been working extremely hard these past three weeks,' he said gently, and she relaxed as she realised he knew the truth.

'Does my misery show on my face?' she asked bitterly.

'It shows on your hands.'

She stared at her chapped skin and the nails which—once long and tapered—were now short and badly broken. Quickly she hid them in the folds of her dress.

'Do not be ashamed to show your hands, my child,' the priest said. 'They are a sign of honest work.'

'Is work honest when it's done under duress? Ramon ordered me to do it.'

'We are all under orders to one extent or another. For you —at this moment—it was Ramon, but at other times you will be ordered by your conscience or by God.'

'Some people consider those two to be the same!'

'Ramon does,' Father Martin smiled. 'He has an exceed-

ingly strong conscience which won't let him rest in the luxury
to which his upbringing accustomed him. He is a good man,
my child. Remember it, and don't judge him harshly because
of the way he has behaved with you.'

Vanessa was angry. 'You sound as if you condone what he's
done!'

'Far from it. But I understand his motivation. And with
understanding comes forgiveness.'

'I haven't had your training, Father,' she said abruptly.
'I'm not as understanding as you.'

There was silence, broken only by the spluttering hiss
from the fire.

'Were it not for Ramon,' Father Martin said slowly, 'many
of my flock would have died of starvation long ago. He has
made everyone in this village and the one below it his responsibility. Even when Indian families come from miles
around to stay here during the worst of the weather, they are
always given food and clothing. More important still, he is
educating the children. Next month one of the huts is being
turned into a schoolhouse and an Indian teacher, whose
training Ramon paid for, is coming here to live.'

'Don't the men work for him?' she asked. 'All the ones in
the valley work for the *hacienda*.'

'The Indians up here farm for themselves—and starve for
themselves, too! But Ramon is teaching them to work with
each other and form a commune. It has been hard to persuade
them—they are a race who prefer to endure their misery
alone—but gradually they have begun to appreciate the benefit of sharing work and dividing gains. Ramon receives no
personal benefit from what he does here, nor from the
hacienda. All the profit that's made is put back into the land
and into equipment.'

'You sound like his publicist,' she commented, and regretted the cheapness of her remark as she saw the compassionate
way he was regarding her.

'I understand why you feel so bitter towards him, my
child, but he does . . .' Blue-veined hands clasped themselves
over the long black cassock. 'I assure you there are areas of
his work that he will not allow anyone to discuss. But his
generosity and depth of caring is there for anyone to see.'

'I don't doubt your word.'

The priest smiled. 'The words aren't an exaggeration either. Do you know he refused to become Ambassador to America because he felt he could do more good here? His family begged him to change his mind, but he wouldn't.'

'Ramon is not a man to listen to anyone.'

'Only to his conscience or his heart.' The priest rose and added more fuel to the fire. 'From what he told me when he drove me here today, I believe he will accept the position next year, when the present Ambassador retires—if his wife would like him to do so.'

Vanessa's muscles contracted involuntarily and she quickly edged her chair closer to the flames, hoping the movement would disguise her reaction.

'I'm surprised Señor de la Rivas will listen to a woman,' she said.

'He will listen to this one,' came the amused reply. 'I never thought to see him quite so tamed by love.'

Again Vanessa reacted physically. But this time she was prepared for it and jumped up to wander round the small room. Could Ramon genuinely care for a girl as immature as Francisca, or was Father Martin so unworldly that he saw every marriage as a union born of ideal love?

'The tougher the man the harder he falls,' she said brightly.

'That will also make him easier to be hurt,' Father Martin added. 'I hope——'

Before he could disclose what his hopes were, Ramon came back, and with a sophistication that Vanessa found surprising, the priest immediately continued speaking to Ramon.

'I hope you found your cheroots? You were gone so long, I wondered if you had returned home for them!'

'The case had fallen under the seat and I had to search for it.' White teeth gleamed as Ramon smiled. 'It's a small vice, Father.' Lighting a cheroot, he settled down.

Vanessa could not bear to look at him. Now that the knowledge of his betrothal was confirmed by Father Martin, her imagination was playing havoc with her. Images of Francisca in his arms, lying against his body, possessed by those long, tapering hands, tortured her. She could take no part in his conversation with Father Martin; it was as much as she could do to remain seated by the fire, her physical appearance calm and relaxed; her mind seething with jealousy.

'You are very quiet, Vanessa.' Ramon broke into her thoughts. 'You are tired, *si*?'

'Yes,' she lied, and rose as he held out the white fur coat.

'We will meet again the day after tomorrow,' Father Martin said as he bade her goodnight.

'I'm counting the hours,' she answered, and looking into his shrewd and kindly eyes, remembered that confession was supposed to be good for the soul. If only she had used her time alone with him to better advantage!

'Come, Vanessa.' Ramon guided her across the icy ground to the Land Rover. He did not speak again until they were halfway up the steep ascent to the lodge. 'What did you think of Father Martin? Is he not an admirable man?'

'Very. And a great fan of yours.'

'I didn't take you to meet him for that reason.'

Surprisingly, she had not thought he had; but she had no intention of telling him so.

'I should have warned him to hold his tongue,' Ramon grunted, still on the same subject.

'I doubt if he would have listened. He isn't the type to be intimidated by you.'

'Those who know me are never intimidated for long. You aren't. You have fought me all the way.'

'Because I hate being controlled.'

'By everyone, or just by me?'

There was a bantering note in his voice that told her she was being teased and because she found it a dangerous intimacy, she dared not respond to it. She looked through the window. The lodge was still some distance away and the engine laboured fiercely, cold from being unused for a few hours.

'It might have been better to have walked,' she commented.

'The ground is too rough for your feet.'

'I walked it carrying pails of water,' she reminded him bitterly.

He flung her a brief look but said nothing, then gave all his attention to the last steep climb. They jerked to a halt a yard away from the front door, and Vanessa jumped to the ground and hurried inside. She took off the fur coat and draped it on a chair. Behind her she heard Ramon come in and do the same with his own jacket.

Josefina was not in her usual night-time position by the fire and Ramon, interpreting Vanessa's look, went into the kitchen and then came out smiling.

'She's making a special stew for tomorrow,' he said, closing the door, 'and it looks as if she decided to sleep beside it!'

'Poor Josefina! She'll be glad to return to the *hacienda*.'

'So will I.'

'It was magnanimous of you to share my hardship,' she said dryly.

'A bit of hardship prevents a man getting soft.'

'I doubt if that could ever happen to you.'

'You still see me as iron?'

'Steel,' she corrected.

'Steel can snap if it's under too much stress,' he said. 'And when I'm near you I——'

'Spare me your compliments, *señor*!'

'I mean them. Don't turn away from me, Vanessa. Listen to me. I want you to come back with me to Lima and——'

'Have you no shame?' she cut in furiously. 'What about Francisca?'

'Why do you keep talking about Francisca? She has nothing to do with what I feel for *you*.' He bridged the distance between them. 'You're so beautiful, Vanessa. When I'm with you my logic drowns in your wonderful eyes. I've never felt this way for a woman. You're all I desire, all I want.'

Desire. Want. Were those the only words he associated with her? Possessive ones that robbed her of her dignity and changed her into an object?

'You'll have to find someone else,' she retorted. 'I'm one woman you'll never possess.'

'I *will*,' he said thickly, and caught hold of her. 'Don't fight me, *querida*. Don't you know how much I need you?'

With his limbs trembling against hers and his eyes half glazed with passion, it would have been difficult not to know, and she felt exultant and shamed. But because shame was the stronger, she pushed desperately against his chest.

'Let go of me, Ramon!'

'No.' He gripped her tighter still. 'Don't fight me, Vanessa. I promise I won't hurt you. Just let me hold you.'

'Never! You've no right.'

Violently she pushed him away, knowing that if she remained close to him she would have no defence against him. Worse still, she would encourage him—and she daren't do that. No matter what the future held for her, she had to retain her pride. Blindly she headed for the door. Pulling it open, she dashed out into the darkness, not caring where she went as long as she went away from Ramon.

'Vanessa, come back!'

His voice rang out behind her, loud in the crisp air. But she disregarded it and went on running, determined to put as much distance between herself and Ramon as she could. Afraid that if she headed for the settlement he would catch up with her long before she even reached it, she made for the rocky path that led upwards beyond their own stone hut. There were lots of boulders here which would give her shelter and she should be able to hide behind one of them and escape his eye.

'Vanessa!' he shouted. 'Where are you? Come back before you freeze to death!'

She crouched lower, determined not to do as he wanted. He had ordered her around long enough. From now on she was free and he would never tell her what to do again.

His footsteps grew louder and she guessed he was walking around the Land Rover to see if she were hiding in it. He gave a muttered imprecation and then moved off, the receding sound of his boots telling her he was making for the settlement.

Gingerly she rose and started to climb. She would stay up here until Ramon came back, then she would go down to the settlement herself and beg Father Martin to put her up for the night. She shivered; not from fear but from cold. In her rush to escape she had been too distraught to think of the weather. But now she felt as if she were being struck by a thousand icicles, each one freezing a globule of her blood until it seemed as if her veins were solidifying. It was a harrowing, crushing cold that made it hard to breathe, and she knew that if she did not want to freeze to death she would have to keep moving.

She swung her arms up and down in an effort to restore her circulation, but all it did was expose more of her body to the air, and she clasped her arms around herself and shrank back against a granite boulder. Her chest seemed to be encased in a strait-jacket of ice; one that was being pulled tighter and tighter until she felt as if her ribs would crack under the pressure. She knew it was only her imagination, but the intensity of the thought was stronger than reality, and though she fought it, her will-power was too sluggish to obey her. Yet she had to fight. If she didn't, reality would congeal into fantasy and she would die.

Fear brought her swiftly to her feet; gave her the strength to move. She couldn't die up here, miles away from those she loved; she couldn't and she wouldn't. She would go back to the lodge. It was no longer important whether or not Ramon was there. All that mattered was to get out of this biting, body-destroying cold.

Turning, she stumbled down towards the path. There were no other huts beyond theirs and because of this the track was almost non-existent, used only by sure-footed llamas and alpacas. 'Of which I'm not one,' she thought wryly as she stumbled and fell.

Sharp flints dug into her knees and tears welled in her eyes, freezing solid the moment they touched her skin. More carefully she continued on her way, looking desperately for a glimmer of light.

Nothing relieved the blackness.

An overcast sky hid the new moon and it was impossible to see more than a few feet ahead. Were there two paths leading to the lodge and could she have taken the wrong one? It was the only possible explanation, and she turned and climbed again, head bent to try and see if there was any division. She stumbled and almost fell, then proceeded to walk more slowly still. It seemed that even the roughest road could be as slippery as glass if it was covered with ice.

A boulder lay ahead of her. It was larger than any she had seen and she could not remember having passed it earlier. Her fear began to grow. Had she taken another wrong turn? It was the only explanation, and once more she began to descend.

A fierce gust of wind almost blew her off her feet and sent her staggering back against the rocky mountain wall. Petrified of being blown down into one of the narrow ravines, she remained pressed against the rock until her heart had ceased thudding against her ribs and resumed a more normal beat, then, still trembling from fright, she inched forward, putting one foot carefully after the other.

It was impossible to know if she was walking on the path or not, for her feet were numb. Her hands were numb too, but this brought a momentary relief from the cold. Yet she had to keep flexing them, for if she didn't, they would get frost-bitten and fall off. Or did that only apply if one got too warm too quickly? The prospect of warmth spurred her on, and flailing her arms and stamping as heavily as she could, she continued moving in the direction of the lodge.

Except that the lodge wasn't there.

Hands clasped to her face, she began to pray, 'Please God, let me turn past the next rock and see some lights. Please don't let me be lost. Please let Ramon find me.'

Ramon . . . somehow it seemed more important to have him close than to escape from him, and she started to call his name. But the wind whipped her voice away, turning it into a thin piping sound like a broken reed.

She breasted another boulder, her eyes staring fixedly ahead, not daring to think what she would do if there was only darkness here too. But darkness there was—a deep, impenetrable wall of black jagged rock. She had stumbled into a cave! Her first feeling of horror, for it seemed almost as if she were walking into a pit—was swamped by the sudden lessening of the wind. She still heard it whistling and howling, but it was no longer around her. It was outside the cave.

Clutching her arms around her shivering body, she took a couple of steps forward. The darkness intensified, and though she knew this was impossible, for black could not become blacker, it definitely appeared to have a different quality about it, caused by the darkness of the atmosphere and a sourish odour that seemed to penetrate her skin. She stopped walking. She would remain as close to the entrance as she could without feeling the wind. In that way she would only have to contend with the temperature, which must be well below zero.

She huddled down on the ground and tried to curl up into as small a bundle as she could. Apart from gaining subconscious comfort from the womb-like position, there was less of her exposed to the cold. If only she had reached for the fur coat on her way out! She thought of it draped carelessly over the chair and could have wept from frustration. If she had to stay here all night she might easily die of exposure. Already she could feel a numbness creeping over her, turning her limbs to lead but freeing them from the unpleasant sensation of burning cold. She giggled. How could cold burn you? She was being fanciful. Yet she had read about freezer burns; had even found evidence of it in some frozen food she had once bought and then returned to the supermarket. It had been lamb chops and the meat had had an unpleasant greyish mark along one side. Was that what would happen to her flesh if she were not found in time? The horror of the thought flooded her with panic. She tried to move but could not do so, and she began to shout Ramon's name again, her cries becoming more and more frenzied.

Even when she realised no one could hear her, she went on shouting, and only when her voice had cracked with the effort did she stop. The wind was howling outside the cave and had it not been for its fierce whine she would have thought herself in a tomb. And how easily this cave could become one, unless she managed to get out of it. There was no succour in its depth nor consolation in its quiet. She must face the wind and ice and fight to stay alive.

Again she went to stand, but nothing happened. Her body would not move.

'Don't panic,' she warned herself. 'You're not paralysed and you won't be stuck here. Just relax for a while and then try again.'

She took a deep breath, then another slower one, and tried to flex her fingers. Sluggishly they responded. Now for her legs. Still nothing. Still inert as two planks.

Planks. Wood. Coffin. Her scalp prickled with the horror of it. 'Careful,' she warned. 'Don't have hysterics or you'll never get out of here. You *can* move. You've got to believe you can.'

Once more she leaned forwards and upwards, using her hands to gain momentum. Painfully she began to drag herself along the floor, inch by bloodied inch, getting closer to the mouth of the cave where the greyness beckoned like the Holy Grail.

As her head emerged from the entrance it met the full blast of the wind and she was thrown back as if she were a sheet of paper. It took her several moments before she had recovered sufficiently to try again and though she was able to get halfway out, the force of the wind flattened her against the rocky wall. Knowing that to continue any further would lead to certain death, and a far more painful one than if she stayed here, she edged backwards into the cave.

'What have I done to myself?' she asked. 'Why didn't I give in to Ramon? Surely love was better than death, even though the love was one-sided?'

Random questions and answers whirled around in her brain like snowflakes in a storm and, like snowflakes, had the same deadening quality. Her fear was gone. She was no longer cold or uncomfortable. Stranger still, she was beginning to feel warm. She put her hands to her face. Moisture trickled on to her lips and she licked them and felt the salt taste of blood. But she didn't feel as if she were bleeding. She touched her fingers across her cheeks and felt damp warmth. She smiled. How funny to be warmed to death by your own blood!

There was the sound of giggling and she looked round, then realised the sound was coming from her own lips. At least she hadn't lost her sense of humour. And it *was* rather funny if one thought about it. Loving Ramon to death, yet choosing death because one didn't want to have him love *you*.

She relaxed against the wall, feeling as comfortable as if she were lying upon a duvet. Her body was no longer a part of her and seemed to be moving along on buoyant waves of air. Yet air was soundless and there was a definite murmuring in the air. She could not hear what it said, yet she knew it was there, comforting her.

Her body continued to float and she tried to turn her head. But she could not move, nor could she open her eyes. All functions were suspended and only her mind seemed capable of action, darting from one thought to another but settling nowhere. She struggled to speak and felt a gentle pressure on her eyelids. It seemed to release a spring and she was able to lift them. But she could not see anything, though the murmur grew louder and became a voice.

'Vanessa! Can you hear me? You're safe, Vanessa. You'll soon be warm.'

Ramon. Happiness bubbled inside her and she made a tremendous effort to speak. But though her mouth moved, no sound emerged.

'You're safe,' Ramon said again. 'You've nothing to worry about.'

Again she tried to speak, but his name hovered above her like a feather. Or was it a snowflake? Ramon. Ramon. Soon there were a hundred snowflakes and then thousands. Thousands and thousands that formed a cloud of white to support her and upon which she drifted down into total unconsciousness.

CHAPTER THIRTEEN

VANESSA was in a never-ending limbo of horror. It could not be a nightmare, for nightmares came to an end, and it could not be a dream, for dreams were pleasant or crazy. Yet this distortion of reality was like a Magritte canvas; seemingly real yet horrifyingly unreal.

Every breath she took was an agony; every movement a descent into Hell. And all without sound. For no matter how much she tried to speak, she was overwhelmed by the effort of breathing.

Suddenly sound returned and she was deafened by it. She longed to retreat into silence again, but there was no going back. The sounds grew louder and there was nothing she could do to stop them. They entered her bloodstream and her brain until she seemed to be dissolving into sound itself. White sound. Like the white world around her and the white arms that were preventing her from moving.

'Sleep,' said a voice. 'You're doing fine, but you must sleep.'

Consciousness, when it came, was a gradual return to awareness. First she felt softness beneath her, then moving her arms gingerly she felt a silken sheet. Next came the light weight of an eiderdown, puffy and yielding as if it were alive. As she was alive.

She opened her eyes and stared at a carved wooden ceiling. She frowned at it, trying to remember if she had seen it before. But she was too tired to think and she closed her eyes again.

'You are awake, I think,' a melodious voice said. 'Ramon will be delighted.'

Swiftly Vanessa opened her eyes again. Warm brown ones stared into hers, then moved back to show they were set in a narrow face with a high forehead. Glossy brown hair swept up and away from it, the way Ramon's did, to proclaim her relationship with him, and her curving smile as she saw that Vanessa was fully conscious confirmed it.

'How do you feel, my dear?'

'I'm not sure.'

Vanessa flexed her limbs and went to sit up. The effort left her exhausted and she lay back upon the pillows until her breathing had steadied.

'I seem to have lost my strength,' she whispered.

'I'm not surprised,' the woman said. 'But you'll soon get it back when you start eating normally. For the past week you have been living on liquids.'

She moved away from the bed and came back with a silver-backed mirror which she held in front of Vanessa's face. A pale triangle was visible in it, with sapphire blue eyes large in a pale face; the whole framed by a mass of unruly mahogany hair.

'You see, you are still very beautiful,' the woman said. 'It's no wonder that——' Abruptly she put down the mirror and sat beside the bed again. 'Doctor Salvez will be here soon. He comes twice a day to see you.'

'So often?'

'You've been very ill. You have a nurse too.'

'What was wrong with me?' Vanessa asked.

'Pneumonia and frostbite. For the first three days Ramon refused to leave your side. Doctor Salvez wanted to take you into hospital, but Ramon wouldn't hear of it. He insisted you remain here. He brought in so much medical equipment he could have opened his own clinic! But he was convinced you would get better care if he were able to look after you himself.'

Vanessa knew she was expected to show a sign of appreciation, but all she could think of was that she would never have been ill had Ramon not taken her prisoner in the first place. Yet to say so at this moment would be singularly inopportune, and instead she pretended an interest in her surroundings.

The room was large and the huge double bed in which she lay was dwarfed by the space around it. The floor was close-carpeted in white—no vivid Peruvian rugs here—and a couple of gilt-framed armchairs, covered in the same rose silk as the drapes, stood on either side of a graceful escritoire. It did not need the faint sound of distant traffic to tell her she was in Lima, nor any imagination that she was in Ramon's house.

'How did I get here?' she asked, genuinely curious.

'Ramon flew you here from Puno. Do you remember anything of the journey?' At the shake of Vanessa's head, the woman went to speak again and then stopped. 'Ramon said I mustn't bother you with questions. He'll be cross with me if I disobey him. He also made me promise to call him the minute you regained consciousness. But unfortunately he is not here—and this will annoy him even more!'

Vanessa did not need to ask why. Ramon wanted to make sure that the story he gave his sister tallied with the one *he* had given. Still, he had nothing to fear. She was far too muzzy in the head to be able to say anything—derogatory or otherwise.

'I've just remembered that I haven't introduced myself,' the woman went on. 'I am Ramon's sister, Consuelo. I hope we are going to be friends.'

Vanessa smiled but said nothing. She could not imagine being friends with this tall, graceful creature who looked like a hothouse flower. The simile made her glance at her hands. They were no longer rough but smooth and pale, the nails filbert in shape.

'I will leave you to rest,' said Consuelo, 'and return when the doctor comes to see you.'

Before the door had closed on her elegant, black-clad figure, Vanessa was asleep. She did not awaken until Doctor Salvez arrived. He was thin-faced and serious in manner and looked, in his dark jacket and striped trousers, more like an undertaker than a doctor.

'You have had a lucky escape,' he said, taking her wrist and feeling her pulse. 'But now I would like you to get out of bed several times each day, and move around.'

'How long will it be before I'm completely well?' Vanessa asked.

'It will be a few weeks before your strength returns fully. But do not be too impatient, *señorita*. You are lucky to be alive. Not many people could survive a night in the *altoplano*.'

'Was I there a whole night?' she asked.

The doctor shook his head after glancing at Consuelo. 'For half the night only. But Señor de la Rivas' quick thinking prevented you from losing your toes and fingers from frostbite. But we will not talk of it now, I think. It is best forgotten.' He put her hand back on the coverlet. 'I won't come back to see you this evening. If I do, you will go on thinking yourself as an invalid.'

'May I get up now?' Vanessa asked as he went to the door.

'By all means.'

'Wait until I fetch the nurse,' said Consuelo.

'I don't need a nurse,' Vanessa replied. 'You heard what the doctor said—I'm not an invalid.'

'Walk before you run,' the doctor cautioned with a smile, and followed Ramon's sister from the room.

Left alone, Vanessa found that her protest that she was well—mildly though it had been made—had exhausted her, and she lay back on her pillows. How unreal everything seemed! It was as if she were not living in the present but was still in the stone lodge high up in the Andes; running away from Ramon because she had so desperately wanted to stay with him. She remembered being in the cave, but had no clear recollection of what had happened afterwards. She vaguely knew she had been in some kind of plastic bubble—an oxygen tent, no doubt—and struggling for breath. The very thought of it brought her out in a sweat, and she forced herself to think of today.

Gently she sat up and swung her feet over the edge of the bed. The room remained motionless and she slid forward and stood up. The walls closed in on her and the ceiling descended. With a gasp she fell back upon the bed. What had the doctor said about her getting up three or four times a day? He was either a fool or a super-optimist!

After a few moments the room ceased its nauseous swinging and she eased up into a sitting position. The large magnificence of her bed made her feel particularly fragile; a fact further increased by her luxurious nightgown: blue chiffon, with pleated skirt and a bodice edged with swansdown. It was like something from a Busby Berkeley musical and the notion made her smile.

The opening of the door stiffened the smile, though it was not Ramon who came in, as she had feared, but Francisca Moyas, her dark eyes full of concern, her arms full of flowers that she placed on the side of the bed.

'I came to the house to leave these for you,' she said huskily, 'but I heard Consuelo talking to the doctor in the *sala*, so I crept up without them hearing me. You have been very ill.'

'It was my own silly fault.' Vanessa avoided meeting the limpid eyes, and wished she knew what explanation Ramon had given his fiancée for her being out on the mountainside.

'Ramon blames himself,' Francisca said in a rush. 'If he had let you leave the *hacienda* with us, none of this would have happened. I suppose he took you to the lodge to stop you from leaving him?'

The sadness in the young voice aroused Vanessa's sympathies. Loving Ramon herself, she knew only too well how the girl felt. And there was no reason why they should both be unhappy. Once before she had tried to tell Francisca the truth, but the girl had refused to believe her. But now it was imperative that she did; not only for her future happiness with Ramon, but for Vanessa's own peace of mind.

'I didn't run away from Ramon because of a lovers' quarrel,' she said. 'I refused to pay him the price he wanted for the clothes I wished to buy, and he was keeping me at the *hacienda* until I'd made a complete set of Indian garments myself.'

'Why?' Francisca was bewildered.

'He thought it would help me to appreciate their value.' Vanessa paused, drew a deep breath and said: 'There was never anything personal between us. When he found me in your car he was angry because I was getting the better of him, and——'

'Ramon wouldn't like that,' Francisca interposed.

'He didn't. That's why he took me to the lodge with Josefina. He knew I'd never be able to escape from there.'

'But you tried!'

'Naturally. I don't like being blackmailed into doing something. I'm used to being my own mistress and . . .' It was a key word and her brain centred on it. 'What I'm trying to tell you, Señorita Moyas, is that I'm not . . . I'm not having an affair with him.'

Francisca looked down at her lap. The parting of her hair was clearly seen: a thin white line as straight and pure as her innocence.

'It's very kind of you to tell me this,' she whispered. 'You are as kind as you are beautiful. As I told you at the *hacienda*, I know that Ramon . . . that he likes pretty women. That's why, when I saw you there, I——' She gave Vanessa an embarrassed glance. 'Please forgive me for what I thought, but . . . I see now that I was wrong.'

'Thank heavens you believe me!' Vanessa was astonished at the relief she felt. She was obviously not the stuff of which mistresses were made.

'It isn't quite as simple as you think.' Francisca spoke again, her almond-shaped eyes enlarged by tears. 'What you've told me makes me happy, but it doesn't alter what Ramon must do.'

Vanessa was puzzled. 'Must do?'

'He's honour bound to marry you.'

'*Me?*'

'He has no choice. Having compromised you, he must ask you to be his wife.'

'That's crazy!' Vanessa remembered Ramon laughing at her when she had threatened to blacken his name for keeping her a prisoner at the *hacienda*. 'No one bothers about that sort of thing nowadays. In fact Ramon and I were discussing it one evening and——'

'Keeping you at the *hacienda* was one thing,' Francisca interposed. 'But taking you to the lodge was quite different.'

'I don't see why. Josefina was with us.'

'I know—And I agree with you.' Francisca was openly crying. 'But it isn't what *we* think that matters. It's what Limoan society thinks. Ramon cannot afford to be involved in a scandal. He's been offered an important Government

post and it is essential for him to retain his good name. The
newspapers reported your arrival from Puno—with pictures
of you in an ambulance and Ramon beside you—and they
are now saying he'll marry you as soon as you are well. For
that reason alone, he feels he must ask you to be his wife.'

Vanessa flinched at the words. *Must ask you.* How humili-
ating to know she was only an obligation to him! Well, he
would soon learn differently.

'I don't give a damn what your society thinks!' she said
aloud. 'I've no intention of marrying a man I—I don't love.
The minute I'm well enough to travel, I'm going back to
England.'

Francisca looked disbelieving. 'You would *refuse* Ramon?'
'Certainly.'

Vanessa clenched her hands beneath the coverlet and
resisted the urge to pull it over her face. She had to see this
conversation through to the end; there was no other way.

'I'm quite willing for everyone in Lima to know he was
prepared to do the right thing,' she continued. 'So he can tell
his friends he asked me to marry him and that I turned him
down.'

'I still cannot . . . Oh, it is too good to be true!'

'Well, I assure you it is.' Vanessa tried to keep her voice
light, but it cracked. 'I'm feeling very tired, Miss Moyas. I
don't think I can talk any more.'

'I understand.' Francisca looked both contrite and guilty.
'Consuelo will be angry with me for coming up to see you
when you are still unwell. I think it would be better if you did
not tell her.'

Vanessa shrugged, past caring what she promised, anxious
only to be alone with her misery.

'I'll never forget you,' Francisca went on, and picked up
the bouquet of flowers. 'I'll give these to a maid to put into
water,' she added, and went out in a flutter of black silk.

It was no less black than Vanessa's mood, and she lay in
the bed and wished it were a magic carpet that could transport her to England. But first she had to live through a meeting with Ramon; that was something she could not avoid, no
matter how hard she tried.

It came about more naturally than she had anticipated.
One moment she was lying with her eyes closed, drifting into

light slumber, and the next she opened them to find him watching her.

She was not the only one who had lost weight, was her first thought as she saw him, for he was considerably thinner. It made his cheekbones look higher and his jaw more prominent, giving one a preview of how he would look in old age. Always handsome, she acknowledged with an upsurge of tenderness, and would have given ten years of her life to have been able to share some part of it with him.

'The doctor says you are much better.'

Ramon's voice was gentle as a violin. He moved closer to the bed but stood rigid, almost as if he were standing to attention.

Small wonder that he was, she thought wryly. He was preparing himself to propose to her and to say goodbye to marrying the girl he loved. Or did he love Francisca? Wouldn't it be more truthful to say that the Peruvian girl would make him the sort of wife he needed? But no, that was untrue. Remembering the impassioned way he had spoken about his love, she knew he was blind to her naïveté and immaturity.

His desire to make love to another woman was easily explained when one realised that, Peruvian behaviour still being predominantly Spanish in custom, his relationship with Francisca was platonic. Put a young and beautiful female in his home—and make that home isolated in the extreme— and one should not be surprised to find him turning to her for satisfaction.

What would have happened between them if he had already been married when they had met? Would he still have found her desirable, or would his desire for her have been more easily controlled? The answers depended on how satisfying he found his relationship with his wife. Father Martin had said Ramon believed in the sanctity of marriage, and she wondered if this would apply if she herself was his wife.

But she loved him too much to take advantage of the proposal he was going to make. Besides, knowing he had been forced into marrying her would prevent her being happy with him. She ran her tongue over her lips. She must say something before he had a chance to speak.

'I'm sorry I caused you so much trouble, Ramon. It was stupid of me to have run out of the lodge the way I did.'

'Very stupid,' he agreed. 'You could have died.'

'I'm tougher than you think.'

'*I* am not.' His voice was low. 'For the first couple of days afterwards—when you were so ill—I didn't think I would be able to——'

'I needn't be on your conscience any longer,' she interrupted lightly. 'I'll soon be perfectly fit and able to go home.'

'You are to regard *my* house as your home.'

She almost faltered but not quite. 'It's . . . it's very kind of you to say that, but I . . . it's out of the question. Your home is beautiful—the little I have seen of it—but I feel a foreigner here.'

'Then we will give you bacon and eggs for breakfast and make you feel you are in England!'

'It would take more than bacon and eggs to do that.'

'I will give you more,' he said huskily, and bent over the bed to catch her hand. 'I will give you everything I have, Vanessa. When I think what you have suffered . . . the agony I put you through . . .' His eyes—dark with pain-filled memories—mirrored his thoughts. 'If I hadn't found you in the cave you would have died. When I think how close you came to it . . .' A shudder racked his body. 'If anything had happened to you, it would have haunted me for the rest of my life.'

'*Nothing* happened to me,' she said. 'I'm completely well. I do wish you wouldn't make a fuss over it. It was just one of those things.'

'Just one of those things that made you rush off like a demented spirit? Don't you know it's only by the grace of God that you weren't frozen to death?' He dropped her hand in a violent gesture. 'How dare you say it's one of those things—*Dios*, I do not understand the English! But no matter, when you are my wife I will learn.'

If Vanessa had not wanted to burst into tears at these words she might easily have given way to hysterical laughter. How typical of the man was his proposal. He was so confident she would accept him that he had not considered it necessary to put the question.

'No, Ramon,' she said quietly, 'I am not going to marry you.'

'You are,' he said equally quietly.

'No,' she repeated, and knew she dared not let this scene go on too long in case she broke down. Yet she had to be careful what she said. He was too intelligent to be fooled. If he guessed she had fallen in love with him, his feelings of guilt would intensify and he would never let her go. Drawing a deep breath, she spoke again.

'Running away from you that night was childish behaviour and I'm ashamed of it. But I found you physically attractive and I was afraid of what would happen if I stayed with you.'

'Nothing would have happened if you had not wanted it to. I am not an animal, Vanessa.'

'Maybe *I* am.' She made a brave attempt at humour, but the bleak look with which he favoured her told her it had not come off. 'I'm trying to be funny, Ramon, because I don't want to be serious.'

'We have to be serious.'

She looked into his face, loving every firm line of it and knowing it would always be engraved in her mind's eye. Naturally he wanted to be serious. He was concerned with his good name and honour, both of which were important to him; not only because of his heritage but because of his political career.

'You may tell your friends and relations that you asked me to be your wife and that I turned you down. Surely that will be enough to satisfy their old-fashioned criteria?'

'Will it be enough to satisfy *you*?' His eyes sparkled with anger. 'Will you be able to return to England and forget me? Take care how you answer that question, Vanessa. Don't forget I've held you in my arms and felt the way you responded to me!'

'It meant nothing,' she lied. 'It was the mood and the moment. We were living in primitive conditions and I—I lost my head.'

'I lost mine the second time I saw you,' he said grimly.

His confession did not surprise her. Ruthless with others, he was obviously equally ruthless with himself. But if only he had said he had lost his heart! Resolutely she pushed aside the thought and concentrated on trying to absolve him from his sense of obligation.

'I am honoured by your proposal, Ramon, but I still can't accept it. What happened at the *hacienda* and the lodge was a—was a kind of madness that would never have happened anywhere else. I don't *want* to get married. I don't want to share my life with any man.' How true that was, she thought bitterly. Not any man; only Ramon. But aloud she said: 'I have never made a secret of the fact that my career means everything to me. That's why I came to Peru. It was my chance to prove to Delphine that I was good enough to become her partner. I'm not her partner yet,' she added, 'no matter what you think to the contrary!'

'And to become her partner means more to you than to be my wife?'

Vanessa moved slightly, but enough for the silk sheet to cover her shaking hands. 'Yes, Ramon, it does.'

His lids lowered, making his expression enigmatic. Never an easy man to understand, at this moment his reaction was a total surprise. She had expected him to show some relief—even gratitude—yet she saw only aloofness and withdrawal. Anger too, which she could not understand. And yet perhaps she did. After all, as Francisca had said, what woman would turn down the chance of becoming Señora de la Rivas? No wonder he was put out.

'We will not prolong this conversation,' he said suddenly, and gave her a bright smile that looked pasted on to his face. 'You have still not recovered from your ordeal and you must take things easy and obey Doctor Salvez. I will——'

A knock at the door made him turn as a dark-haired maid paused on the threshold and said that a Señor Riversdale wished to see the Señorita.

'Don?' Vanessa exclaimed, and suddenly felt as if sanity were returning to her life. 'Oh, please, I'd love to see him.'

'It is better if he comes back in a couple of days, when you are more rested,' said Ramon.

'Oh no!' Vanessa sat up straight. 'Please let me see him now.'

Ramon's lips thinned, then he tersely commanded the maid to bring the Señor upstairs.

Alone again with Vanessa, he stood in the centre of the room, his profile towards her, his rigid bearing indicative of his barely controlled anger. The presumption of his behaviour—that he should think he could control whom she saw and when—suddenly gave her an idea. It was frequently used but was invariably effective. Jealousy always was.

'Don would have been hurt if I'd refused to see him,' she murmured.

'Another day or so would have made little difference.'

'Yes, it would. He's a very good friend of mine. Very good,' she repeated, and looked away from him as though embarrassed.

'Good friends is an expression that has another meaning these days,' said Ramon. 'And for someone who professes to be more interested in her career . . .'

'That doesn't mean I live like a nun!'

For an instant he was silent, forbidding as an Inca warlord; then he faced her, as disdainful as he had been the night they had first met.

'Am I to assume he is—has been your lover?'

This was having her plan carried too far. But to say no would be to abandon it, so she was forced into prevarication.

'You have no right to question me about my private life.'

'I have every right. A moment ago you refused to become my wife because of the importance of your career.'

'My career has nothing to do with my love life.'

'Yet you refused *me*?'

'I don't want to get married. That doesn't mean I don't want a lover!'

Before Ramon could reply, Don strode in. He looked so exactly as Vanessa had remembered him that she felt as though she were turning back the clock and was once again the carefree, heart-free young woman who had just arrived in Peru. She greeted him warmly, hugging him and patting the side of the bed for him to sit beside her.

'I understand you saved Vanessa's life,' Don said to Ramon, after she had introduced them.

'Don't believe all you read in the newspapers,' Ramon replied crisply. 'They like to exaggerate everything.'

'I doubt if they did so this time. A night outdoors in the Andes would freeze a polar bear!' Don turned back to Vanessa. 'I can understand you going to the *hacienda*, but what made you visit such a primitive settlement?'

At a loss to know how to answer, she looked quickly in Ramon's direction.

'You must blame her visit on the curiosity of women,' he

said, coming to her rescue. 'Vanessa wished to see the actual habitat of the llama, and as I had to go to this particular village, she insisted on coming with me.'

'Ramon takes a priest there once a month,' Vanessa added, 'and that gave me the idea of going along with them.'

'A Father Martin,' Don murmured. 'He was also in the papers. He came back to Lima in the same plane with you.' Grey eyes studied her intently. 'I got the impression he did so because he thought you were dying.'

It was Vanessa's first intimation of how near death she had been, and it made Ramon's proposal of marriage even more understandable.

'That was also a newspaper exaggeration,' she said hurriedly. 'You know how they like to make everything a great drama. Luckily Ramon found me in time and I'm none the worse for the mishap.'

'Mishap!' Ramon exploded the word, then caught himself up, both mentally and physically, for he straightened his shoulders and looked his most imperious. 'It is a good thing the human mind has the capacity to forget, otherwise I doubt if Vanessa would describe her experience on the mountainside as a mishap.'

'I'd rather not describe it at all.' She was beginning to feel faint; her earlier scene with Francisca, and now this one, was threatening to sap what little strength she had.

As always Ramon was instantly alive to her mood, and concern for her overlaid his hauteur. 'You are tired—I can see it on your face. I suggest Mr Riversdale comes back another time.'

'No, no.' She was not going to lose the barrier of Don so easily. 'I'll be fine in a moment. I'll just let Don do the talking.'

There was a noticeable glitter in Ramon's eyes; as if he knew he was being dismissed. 'Then I will bid you both goodbye. I won't be seeing you for a few days, Vanessa. I have to go to New York on business. I hope that on my return you will be considerably improved. Goodbye, Mr Riversdale.'

The door closed behind him and Don let out a relieved breath.

'So that's the great de la Rivas. He has quite a reputation

in Peru, you know. Informed circles think he'll be the next President.'

But Vanessa was not interested in Ramon's future. It was her own that concerned her. 'I have to leave here, Don,' she said. 'Right away.'

'Come again?' He was startled.

'I don't want to be here when Ramon returns from New York.'

'You aren't well enough to go back to England. Which reminds me, I had lunch at the Bolivar the other day and collected some small mail for you. I remembered you telling me your lady boss was going to write to you there.'

'How thoughtful of you! I'd forgotten all about it.'

Taking the envelope from him, Vanessa opened it and read the contents. Shock, disappointment and then anger overtook her in varying degrees.

'What is it?' Don asked, seeing the different emotions that crossed her face. 'Bad news?'

'For me,' said Vanessa. 'Not for Delphine. Apparently she went to Sardinia to convalesce and while there met some Frenchman who owns a chain of stores on the Continent. He wants to start up in England and made her an offer for the boutique.' Vanessa looked at the letter again. 'A wonderful offer that I couldn't possibly turn down,' she read aloud. 'I've told Claude you're absolutely marvellous and he's most anxious for you to remain with him. I'm sure you won't have any difficulty in getting him to make you the manageress.'

Vanessa's voice shook so much that she could not continue. Manageress, when she had been hoping—had been certain—of becoming a partner! Well, she had no one to blame but herself. And from now on she would work for herself too. Better to begin in a garret on her own than run the most exclusive shop for someone else.

'Is that all she says?' Don asked.

'The funny part comes next,' Vanessa said dryly. 'She says this Frenchman plans to concentrate on French and Italian wear only, so I shouldn't bother buying any Peruvian clothes other than what I'd bought before I received her letter.'

'She's a cool customer, isn't she?' Don remarked. 'Sending you all the way here and then calmly selling the business behind your back.'

'It's *her* business,' Vanessa shrugged. 'Though I must admit I'm pretty shattered.'

'Will you work for this Claude?'

'No. From now I'm going to be my own boss.'

'From the look of you you need a long holiday first.' He regarded her reflectively. 'Why not stay on in Lima? I'm sure I can wangle you a job with the Trade Council.'

The idea of living in the same city as Ramon was impossible. 'No, thanks, Don. I still want to go home and I still want to leave this house. Do you know of somewhere inexpensive where I can stay? Delphine will pay all my bills, but I don't want to run up a large one for her.'

'I don't see why not.' He half smiled. 'It would serve her right if you booked into a suite at the Lima-Sheraton!'

She smiled back. 'Don't tempt me. She'd die of shock if I did so!'

'Would you object to a private house?' Don ventured. 'A friend of my chief—a Señora Lopez—was recently widowed and needs some extra cash. I'm sure she'd be delighted to have you.'

'And I'd be delighted to go. It sounds much better than a hotel.'

'I still don't see why you can't stay on here. After all, you were Señor de la Rivas' guest at his *hacienda*. A few more days here won't make any difference to him.' Don's voice trailed away as he saw Vanessa's expression and he looked distinctly embarrassed. 'You and he aren't . . .'

'No,' she replied, 'we aren't. But I do want to leave before he comes back from New York.'

'You can't go without telling him. He's an important man and I don't want to antagonise him. I'm speaking in my official capacity,' he explained hastily.

'I understand,' she said. 'I'll explain to his sister and make sure she knows it was *my* decision to go, not yours.'

'Fine. Then I'll have a word with Señora Lopez about renting you a room. Will the end of the week be all right?'

'Make it the day after tomorrow.'

Don looked as if he wanted to say more, but then thought better of it and nodded.

'I'll pick you up in the afternoon, then, and take you there.'

Vanessa agreed, glad that things seemed to be falling into

place, though she knew she would not have complete peace of mind until she was out of Ramon's orbit entirely And that meant England and the resumption of her career. Only in work did she stand a chance of coming to terms with a life without him.

Two days later she left Ramon's home. Consuelo was extremely upset to see her go, more particularly since she did so while her brother was away.

'He will blame me for letting you leave,' his sister protested. 'At least wait until you have seen him.'

'That's precisely what I don't want to do.' Vanessa was reluctant to say more, not sure if Consuelo knew that Ramon had asked her to marry him. However, the woman's next words showed she was in her brother's confidence.

'He cannot understand why you refused to be his wife. You must be the only girl in Peru who would have turned him down!'

'A marriage won't work if two people don't love each other equally.' Vanessa could have bitten off her tongue as soon as she had spoken, but having committed herself, it was impossible to retreat. 'You do agree with me, don't you?'

'Of course. What you say makes sense. If one partner loves the other more, then neither of them will be completely happy.'

Hearing her own feelings confirmed in no way lessened Vanessa's depression. 'I hope you won't tell Ramon what I said? I don't want him to know I talked about——'

'Never!' Consuelo interrupted emphatically. 'It shall be between *us* and no one else.'

A few hours later Vanessa climbed into Don's car and was driven away. It was only as they bowled along the short drive that she had her first glimpse of the exterior of Ramon's home, and appreciated its size and grandeur. Richly carved columns, wide verandas and delicate archways and balustrades embellished what looked to be a miniature palace. Soon it would be Francisca's home. Tears filled her eyes and she closed them in case Don glanced her way and saw them. How she envied the girl her position; not because of the wealth that the house indicated, but because of the man who was its master.

'I'd be happy to live with him in a garret,' she thought

despairingly, and wished she had not run away from him that night at the lodge. Had she stayed, she would at least have had one special memory to sustain her in her bleak future.

CHAPTER FOURTEEN

WITHIN an hour of meeting Señora Lopez, Vanessa felt as if she had come home. The house was unpretentious and set in a small, flower-filled garden. The neighbourhood was not as exclusive as the one she had left, but it was residential and her hostess—one could hardly call her a landlady—was a charming, middle-aged woman who spoke excellent English with an American accent.

She showed Vanessa to her room and indicated her willingness to serve her all her meals there.

'Señor Riversdale has told me you still need to rest,' she added, 'and it is no trouble for me to have your food sent up.'

'It's very kind of you.' Vanessa was grateful. 'But I don't want to be treated like an invalid. The sooner I can return to normal living the better.'

'It is unwise to rush things.'

'And equally unwise to let oneself get spoiled!'

But words were easier than action, and for the rest of the week Vanessa was too tired to do more than get up at midday and crawl thankfully back to bed immediately dinner was over.

By Saturday she was feeling a great deal better, though restless too, for she was sure Ramon was back in Lima and could imagine the anger with which he had learned of her departure during his absence. Knowing him, she was convinced he would seek her out at once and demand an explanation, and each time she heard the telephone or doorbell ring she waited apprehensively for his appearance. But at least she was on neutral ground here and not his own territory, which would make it easier for her not to be overwhelmed by his dictatorial manner.

However, the weekend passed without a word from him and she began to feel less afraid; less afraid but considerably more unhappy, which only went to show how inconsistent she was. The sooner she was in the cool clime of her native land, the sooner she would regain her British phlegm.

'I still think you're foolish to rush back,' Don commented on Monday evening, when he came to see her and she told him of her desire to leave. 'It isn't even as if you have a job waiting for you back home.'

'All the more reason for me to go. I'm not a lady of leisure, you know.'

'There's no point rushing back to work and then collapsing. If you're serious about starting on your own, you'll need all the strength you've got.'

There was so much truth in what he said that she gave in. Another week of rest and she would be far better equipped to face the problems of finding workspace, persuading her bank manager to give her a loan and designing a collection with which to begin her onslaught on the fashion market.

If only she could conjure up more enthusiasm at the prospect! What had happened to all her ambitious plans? Could loving Ramon have turned all her dreams to ashes? Was she so much a slave to her emotions that she would be content to discard her career for marriage? With a sigh she knew she was. Mother Nature had been going too long to let herself be vanquished by emancipated women. One had to fight her with more cunning.

Three more days went by. The weather was warm, though the evenings were cool. Vanessa spent most of her days in the garden reading the English books Don had brought her and resolutely refusing to sit and day-dream; that was for people with happy thoughts.

But inevitably Ramon would come into her mind and she would wonder what he was doing and whether he and Francisca had settled on the date for their wedding. It was a prospect that filled her with despair: not only for her own sake but for his. She wanted his happiness, but did not believe he would find it with a girl who, even on second acquaintance, had seemed like a charming child.

On Friday afternoon, unannounced and unexpected, Father Martin came to see her.

As he walked across the lawn, his spare, cassocked figure brought with it such a vivid memory of the Andean village where they had met that she paled visibly.

Seeing it, he looked anxious and reached for her hands.

'I hope you do not object to my coming here, my child? But I was in Lima and did not feel I could leave without seeing you.'

'I'm delighted you've come. Please sit down.'

He did so, then surveyed her. 'You are lucky to be alive.'

'I know.' She hesitated. 'If Ramon hadn't found me, I would have died.'

'Then you would have been on his conscience for ever.'

Something in Father Martin's voice told her he knew why she had run away from the lodge that night. Yet she did not want him to think badly of Ramon, and she said quickly:

'It was my own fault. I had no reason to run away.'

'You had every reason. You were alone with a man of passion and you were afraid.'

She was taken aback. 'He . . . he told you what happened?'

'Yes.'

Father Martin paused, as if expecting her to speak. When she didn't, he fingered his rosary and pursed his lips. There was something in his expression that told Vanessa he was not praying, and she waited tensely for what he was going to say.

'Within a few days of confining you in his home,' the priest began, 'Ramon deeply regretted it.'

'I'd never have guessed,' she said bitterly. 'Why didn't he let me go?'

'Don't you know?'

Her cheeks grew warm. Though the confessional made sure that even the most saintly of priests was aware of sensual motivations, she nonetheless found it embarrassing to admit Ramon's passion for her.

'He loves you, my child,' Father Martin said into the silence. 'That was why he couldn't bear to send you away. He told me this when we were driving to the settlement. I warned him he was doing wrong in not giving you your freedom, and he agreed with me.'

'But still did nothing about it!'

'He was going to. He told me he would set you free and take you back to Lima. He wanted to court you properly and show you how much you meant to him.'

Vanessa tried not to believe what Father Martin was saying, but his words brought Ramon vividly to mind. To court her properly. It was so exactly the sort of thing he would say! Yet it couldn't be true. He loved Francisca. Father Martin must have misunderstood him. Either that, or Ramon had lied. Yes, that was it. Ramon had felt so guilty at keeping her a prisoner that he had wanted the priest to think he had done so because he had loved her.

'I don't think he meant it,' she said slowly. Then not wishing to imply that Ramon had deliberately lied, she added: Perhaps you misunderstood him.'

'He was too outspoken for me to do that,' came the dry answer. 'Besides, it is part of my profession to have people confide in me.'

'He's engaged to Señorita Moyas,' Vanessa persisted.

'To Francisca? No; no, that cannot be.'

'She told me so.'

'But he loves *you*! You're the one he has asked to marry.'

With a murmur of anguish she jumped to her feet. She wanted to run away, but knew it would be fatal to do so. Instead she kept her face averted, her fingers plucking at the basket-work chair. Beads clicked and she knew the priest had stood up too. She prayed for him to go, but when he moved, it was in her direction.

'When Ramon told me this morning that you had refused to marry him,' Father Martin said, 'I could not understand it. I am an old man, I know, but not so old that I cannot recognise love when I see it. And you do love Ramon. I saw it on your face when you were with him at my table.'

'You're wrong.'

'No, my child. Fool yourself and Ramon, if you wish, but do not try to fool me.'

Once again Vanessa was the victim of her own embarrassment. What was there about the cassock that made lying so untenable for her?

'I'm sorry, Father. You're right. But I've tried so hard to stop loving him that I can't even bear to admit it to myself.'

'But where is the problem? If you love each other——'

'We don't!' She swung round. 'That's what I'm trying to make you see. Ramon only asked me to marry him because he felt he'd compromised me.'

'How?'

'By keeping me at the *hacienda*.'

'But the servants were there. And Josefina was with you at the settlement.'

'Servants aren't considered suitable chaperones,' she explained.

'Suitable by whom?'

'Limoan society.'

Father Martin seemed unable to speak and she filled in the silence, anxious to put an end to the conversation. They were going round in ever-decreasing circles and she was afraid of being choked by them.

'That's why he proposed to me,' she added. 'Because he's a man of honour. But he loves Señorita Moyas.'

'There are two things wrong with what you have said, my child. Ramon does not love Francisca, nor would he ask to marry a woman he did not genuinely want to be his wife. He regards marriage as a sacred bond. Believe me, child, I know what I'm saying. The woman who bears Ramon's name will have his devotion until the day he dies.'

'But Francisca *told* me they love each other.' Tears blurred Vanessa's vision and she moved distractedly. 'I wasn't feeling very well at the time—I'll admit that—but I didn't imagine the conversation.'

'I am sure you didn't.' Smooth as syrup the placatory words oozed over her. 'When did she speak to you of this?'

'Several times. At the *hacienda* and then again here.'

'You mean she has been here to see you?' Father Martin sounded surprised.

'Not since I moved,' Vanessa explained, 'but at Ramon's house. She brought me flowers.'

'Beware of those who come bearing gifts,' Father Martin misquoted to suit his purpose. 'I can assure you she was lying. She wished to have you out of Ramon's life and——'

'His sister wouldn't lie too,' Vanessa cut in.

'Consuelo said the same as Francisca?'

'Not in those words, but she said he—he doesn't love me.'

'That cannot be!' Dark skirt swirled as the priests's agitation matched Vanessa's. 'I spoke to her myself an hour ago and she said the exact opposite. That you had found Ramon's love a burden and had gone away because of it.'

Vanessa tried to recall the precise words she had said to

Consuelo, but could not do so. Yet she knew what she had not said, and she half shook her head.

Seeing the movement, Father Martin spoke. 'I may have got the words wrong, but the gist of what I was told was perfectly clear. You said a marriage where only one partner loved was intolerable for you and——'

'*My* love for Ramon!' Vanessa burst out. 'Not his for me. That's what I meant. When I spoke to Consuelo I didn't even know he cared for me then. I still don't. I know you've said so, but——'

'Have faith, my child.'

'In you?'

'In God.' The beads of the rosary clinked. 'May I tell Ramon to come and see you?'

She thought for a moment, then shook her head. Disappointment deepened the lines on the face in front of her and she hastily put out her hand.

'I'm not saying no, but I . . . I still can't take it all in. I need to have more time.'

'Not too much time. Ramon is an unhappy man.' Dark eyes scrutinised her. 'Or is it that you would like to make him suffer a little?'

'To pay him back, you mean?' She shook her head. 'I'd never want to do that. At one time I did, but not from the moment I fell in love with him.'

'Then I will leave you to decide when you are ready to see him.'

With a softly spoken blessing Father Martin left, and Vanessa sank down on to the deck chair. She tried to reassess all she had learned. If the priest was right, it explained a great deal about Ramon's behaviour. Knowing he loved her made her see things with a different perspective; she could now think of his lovemaking and her own passionate response to it—with pleasure instead of shame.

She jumped up, almost ready to see Ramon—but not quite. There were other things to think about first: her work as a designer; how much she would miss her sister and the rest of her family; whether she would be able to settle in a foreign country and adapt to an entirely different way of living.

But what alternative did she have? To return to the bleak

future she had envisaged for herself until Father Martin—wonderful interfering old man that he was—had walked back into her life?

Joy began to course through her, rushing with more force as she let down her defences. She no longer had to fight her love. She could admit it openly; respond without fear.

The gate squeaked open and she turned towards it, her heart racing. The sight of the postman only steadied it momentarily, for she knew it would soon be opened again by Ramon. Father Martin was not going to keep silent for long, and if she did not go to Ramon, then he would make sure that Ramon came to *her*.

Remembering the many times he had kissed her, the way she had rebuffed him when he had asked her to be his wife, she was overwhelmed with remorse.

'I love him,' she whispered aloud, savouring the words. 'I love him, and at last I can tell him.'

Not giving herself time to think, she went to her room for a cardigan, told Señora Lopez she was leaving the house for an hour or so and set out in search of a taxi cab. Luckily she found one cruising down the road and within a quarter of an hour was deposited outside the ornate gates leading to Ramon's house.

Walking up the immaculately kept drive to the imposing front door, her confidence waned. Her heart was no longer racing but thumping so heavily that she did not hear the bell ring as she pressed her finger on it. Perhaps she should go away and come back later? She needed more time to think; had to find the best way of telling Ramon what she felt.

She was already several yards from the door when it opened and, glancing round at the impassive-faced servant, saw her behaviour as so ludicrous that she turned back. She had come to see Ramon and see him she would!

'Is Señor de la Rivas at home?' she asked huskily.

The man nodded and motioned her to enter, then led her across the mosaic-tiled floor to a large library. It had none of the gloomy magnificence of the one at the *hacienda* and looked as if it were used for more functional purposes. An electric typewriter stood on the rosewood desk and several box files were ranged alongside the hand-tooled books that covered the length of one wall.

The mirror above the mantelshelf caught her attention and she peered in it to check her appearance, wishing she had taken time to change into something prettier than the plain skirt and blouse she had put on for her day in the garden. The simple lines exaggerated her slenderness and the open collar showed the hollows at the base of her throat. Still, Ramon had seen her looking far worse.

'Vanessa?' His deep voice brought her back to the present and through the mirror she saw him coming towards her. His eyes were bloodshot—as if he hadn't slept well for a long time—and the lines either side of his mouth had become deeply indented grooves.

'When I heard you were here I couldn't believe it,' he said. 'Is anything wrong?'

'No, I'm fine.' She paused. 'I came because . . .'

She was unable to continue and without waiting to be told, she sank on to the nearest chair. Ramon remained standing, looking immeasurably taller and very aloof. It was impossible to imagine him being overcome by passion; shaking with the desire to possess her. This man looked as if he needed no one; cared for no one.

'Father Martin was wrong,' she thought in a panic. 'Ramon doesn't love me. I should never have come here. I must get away before I make a complete idiot of myself.'

'You still look far from well.' Ramon broke the silence. 'I think it was unwise of you to have left my house as quickly as you did. When I returned from the States I was surprised to find you had already gone.'

'It seemed the best thing to do.'

'I don't agree. Though you didn't wish to marry me, there was no reason why you couldn't have remained in my home.'

She shook her head. 'Believing what I did, it was impossible for me to stay here.'

'Then why are you here now?' he asked abruptly.

She longed to say, 'Because I love you,' but could not bring herself to say the words so baldly.

'I—I came to—to tell you why I left,' she stammered.

'I know why you left,' he said harshly. 'Because you couldn't bear to look at me. Because seeing me reminded you of how badly I had treated you. *Dios*!' It was a sound of anguish. 'Do you think me so stupid that I need to be told again?'

He swung away from her and she stared at his broad back, not sure if its trembling movement was caused by her tear-filled vision. She blinked. The blur had gone, but the tremble remained and, seeing it and knowing the reason, her tears returned.

She drew a deep breath. It was now or never. Afraid that if she hesitated it would be never, she let the words tumble out, not caring if she made sense, knowing only that there was no more room for pride.

'You don't know the reason at all, Ramon. I didn't leave here because I hated you but because I loved you! Because I was afraid that if I went on staying here I would agree to marry you.'

He whirled round, his eyes ablaze. 'You love me? You love me and yet you refused to marry me? I don't understand.'

'That's what I've come here to explain.'

'I don't want to hear it! I don't care about anything except that you've finally admitted you love me. Nothing else matters.'

Before she could say another word she was crushed against his chest, his thudding heartbeats merging with her own. The warmth of his body enveloped her and she moved her hands up inside his jacket to press them against his shirt. She felt the roughness of hair beneath the silk and gave a little sigh of pleasure.

'I am curious to know why you thought I asked you to marry me, if I did not love you?'

'Because of your career. Francisca said you'd been offered a post in your Government and——'

'Francisca again?' The golden glints in his eyes were fast being superseded by the darkness of anger. 'When did she see you?'

Haltingly Vanessa told him, trying to gloss over the girl's duplicity but not succeeding.

'I always knew she wanted to marry me,' he said grimly, 'but I had no idea she would be jealous enough to pretend she had already been asked!'

'She was very convincing.'

'Obviously.' The golden glints were coming back again.

'And you think I would have married you in order to stop a lot of old ladies from gossiping?'

'It made sense. You've got a lot of pride.'

'Pride makes a poor bedfellow,' he said. 'And to marry a woman I do not love . . . She would have remained untouched for ever!'

'Then I'm glad that wasn't the reason you proposed to me!'

His laugh was triumphant. '*You* won't remain untouched, my darling!'

Once again he drew her close, his hands gentle but his mouth hard. Willingly, eagerly, she parted her lips, wanting to show him how much she loved him and how much she regretted the many times she had fought him. Feeling her response, his own lips softened, moving across hers lightly, as he spoke against them.

'I have made love to many women, Vanessa, but I have never *been* in love. Nor have I ever asked any woman to be my wife. Until I asked *you.*'

'And then I turned you down.' She shivered at the memory.

'It was one of the worst moments of my life,' he confessed. 'Though the very worst was when you ran out of the lodge and I couldn't find you.'

With a murmur she pressed closer to him and once more he took possession of her mouth. She felt the warm softness of his lips and a spasm contracted her body.

'Darling,' he said thickly, and his own body moved in unison with hers. 'Darling, I . . .'

With a soft imprecation he suddenly let her go. Vanessa looked at him in surprise and saw the self-same desire on his face that she had seen the night she had ran away from the lodge. Except that now she no longer had to run. She could stay and glory in his desire for her; show her own need too, without any feeling of shame.

'I won't push you away this time,' she whispered. 'Kiss me, Ramon.' She went to put her arms around his neck, but he unclasped them and held them away.

'No, my angel. I daren't go on kissing you. If I do, I won't vouch for what will happen.'

She smiled in disbelief. 'Here?'

'Here,' he replied solemnly. 'I understand it's highly satisfactory to make love on the floor!'

As he spoke he caught hold of her hands and began to pull her down, grinning broadly as he saw her expression. 'It is wrong of me to tease you,' he chuckled, 'I merely want you to sit beside me on the settee.'

Close together on the velvet-covered seat, he lifted her fingers to his lips. He said nothing and seemed content to savour her nearness. She was content too, happy to watch him and to know he was hers. Yet never solely hers. Ramon was too committed to helping his people ever to belong solely to one woman. Loving him, she must also learn to share him; to help him with his work.

'There were so many times when I wanted to tell you I loved you,' he said into the silence. 'But I wouldn't let myself do it while I was still forcing you to stay at the *hacienda*.'

'You should have let me escape with Francisca,' she reminded him.

'I know. But I was so furious to think you wanted to leave me—just when I was beginning to think you'd started to care for me—that I lost my temper and my senses. I determined to keep you with me until I'd made you love me. That's why I took you to the settlement.'

'And made me work like a slave,' she reproached.

'I was insane,' he admitted. 'I wanted to hurt you the way you'd hurt me. And instead all I managed to do was to make you hate me.'

'Never that,' she said quickly.

'I deserved your hate,' he asserted. 'When I think what I did to you . . .'

'Don't!' She turned her face into the side of his neck. He smelled of warmth and an indefinable odour that was wholly his. Her bones seemed to melt as her nostrils savoured him, and she touched the side of his face.

'Don't think of the past, Ramon. It's over.'

'But not forgotten. I want our marriage to be a partnership, Vanessa. I know you think I'm autocratic—and from your point of view I probably am—but your spirit and intelligence are two things I love most about you, and I'll never do anything to minimise them. I'm not saying we won't fight, but I *am* saying I'll always respect your right to have an equal say in what we do and how we live.'

'You mean you won't mind if I go on being Delphine's partner?' she asked, straight-faced.

'Don't keep reminding me of my stupidity,' he said. 'If I hadn't been obsessed by you, I'd have believed you from the beginning. But if I'd admitted to myself that you weren't her partner, I'd have had to let you go.' His eyes narrowed. 'If you wish to have a boutique of your own, *querida*, I will buy one for you. I am not saying it because I want to disarm you. I mean it, Vanessa.'

'My marriage is likely to take up all of my time.'

'I find the thought entrancing.' His voice was deep. 'But I know you too well to believe you.' He gave her a sidelong glance. 'The Government are forming a special department to deal with all our crafts, and they intend launching a strong sales drive in all the Western countries. If need be, they'll even open their own boutiques.'

'That's wonderful news! Aren't you delighted?'

'Naturally. It's what I've always been demanding.'

'Have they asked you to run it?' she continued, seeing this as the logical outcome.

'I have been given the choice of two positions,' he said slowly. 'To take charge of this new Department or to go to America as our Ambassador. I have promised to give the President my decision in a few days.'

She had a strong suspicion that he was waiting for her to make some comment, but she was determined to remain neutral. This was Ramon's life and he must be the one to decide what he wanted to do.

'Which one are you going to accept?' she asked without any expression.

'We will decide together.' His eyes appraised her, seeing the flush on her cheeks and the beautiful line of her neck. 'You will be the most entrancing Ambassador's wife in the whole of Washington,' he murmured.

'Is that what you want for me? To show me off and have other men envy you?'

'I want what *you* want.'

'I'm not a jewel that has to be shown off. I'm a woman, and I want the man I love to feel he's doing a worthwhile job. If you see your future in the Diplomatic Service, then fine. But if you want to continue your work with the Indians, I'm happy to go back to the *hacienda*.'

'You'd do that for me? Give up living in a big city and spend your life in the wilds of——'

'I'd live with you in a stone hut,' she interrupted.

'But I'd carry the water!' he replied, and gave a triumphant laugh. 'You're an incomparable woman, my darling. I don't know any other one who'd give up the limelight as easily as you.'

'It needn't be for ever. When we're too old for the rigours of the Andes we can always live it up in Washington!'

'If I head the new Department,' he said softly, 'we'll be spending a great deal of time travelling round the world to establish trade centres. It's my assistants who'll be living in the Andes!'

'Ramon!' She gave him a reproachful look. 'Why didn't you say that in the beginning?'

'I didn't want to influence you.'

He gripped her hand so tightly that she thought her fingers would crack. Then the pressure eased and he raised her hand and kissed her palm.

'I will expect you to work with me,' he said casually. 'The designs you created at the *hacienda* were remarkable. I'm sure that given time, you will be able to produce a whole range of new products for us.'

'I'm sure I can,' she answered, and wondered what he would say if she told him she was thinking in terms of dark-eyed, golden-skinned children.

Something in her tone must have given her away, for he chuckled and pulled her on to his lap. But he still kept a tight control over his emotions, though the nerve that throbbed in the side of his cheek told her what an effort it was for him to do so.

'If you'd told me all this the day you proposed to me,' she said, 'I'd have fallen into your arms like a ripe peach!'

'I thought you'd be scared off if you knew how much I loved you.'

'But you weren't scared of proposing!'

'I had no choice. I was even more scared that if I didn't, you'd rush back to England. I thought that if you knew I wanted to marry you, you'd at least start thinking of me as something less than an ogre!'

She sighed. 'I thought of you as another woman's property.'

Ramon started to smile and the curve of his mouth did something peculiar to her insides. Darn his self-control! Did she still look so fragile that he thought she would faint if he kissed her properly?

'Hold me close,' she begged.

'Not yet.' He played with a tendril of her hair. 'How soon will you marry me?'

'I—I don't know. I'd like . . . I always thought my sister would be able to see me married.'

'I'll invite her to stay here as my guest.'

'She has a family.'

'No matter. Your family will be mine. If it makes you happy to have a hundred relatives here, then so be it.'

Vanessa giggled. 'You'd soon get fed up with that!'

'On the contrary. I'd take you off for a honeymoon and they'd be able to entertain themselves!'

'What a lovely idea!'

'I've got an even better one. We can get married at once and I'll take you to England by ship. It will give you a chance to get your strength back.'

'Perhaps I should get back my strength *before* I marry you?' she suggested humorously.

His eyes glinted. 'I won't make any demands on you, my dearest. Just let me put my ring on your finger and I'll be content to wait.'

'*You* may be, but I won't!'

She caught hold of his shoulders and pulled him down. He resisted and then, seeing the look in her eyes, shook his head.

'You're playing with fire,' he warned huskily.

'Burn me,' she replied, and raised her mouth to his.

With a savage movement he covered her lips, the pressure of his own so heavy that her mouth parted. His breath was warm inside her, but there was still too much of her that was empty; that needed to be filled by him. Only him. No other man would do.

'Vanessa!' It was a deep-throated cry and seemed to be torn from him. He eased away from her again and pulled her into an upright position. 'I will talk to Father Martin about arranging our wedding. Until then, you are going to stay with Consuelo. I don't trust myself to have you here.'

With trembling hands she straightened the collar of her dress. 'You're an anachronism, Ramon. In this day and age men don't usually behave like you.'

'Perhaps if our courtship had been more normal I wouldn't be behaving like this either! But it began so badly that I want to show you I have *some* control over myself.'

Rising, he drew her up with him and gently led her to the door. At the threshold he stopped and looked into her eyes.

'No regrets, my darling? Once you're my wife there'll be no turning back. For me, marriage is for ever.'

'The nicest words in the language,' she whispered. 'I can't think of anything better than spending my life with my wonderful savage.'

'Your what!'

'You, my Inca war-lord. My savage aristocrat!'

'A very tamed one, where you're concerned,' he chuckled.

'Not too tame, I hope?'

The burning brightness of his eyes gave her the answer, and with a happy sigh she gave him her hand and let him lead her out.

Best Seller Romances

Romances you have loved

Mills & Boon Best Seller Romances are the love stories that have proved particularly popular with our readers. They really are "back by popular demand." These are the other titles to look out for this month.

THE WOOL KING
by Kerry Allyne

Tracey didn't want a guardian; in particular she didn't want that guardian to be Ryan Alexander, nor did she want to go and live on his vast sheep station in the outback. But there wasn't much she could do about any of it without hurting her sister. So she had quite enough to contend with even before she found herself having to fight a growing attraction towards Ryan!

GIANT OF MESABI
by Janet Dailey

It was Kurt Matthews whom Alanna wanted and intended to marry — but his brother Rolt who blackmailed her into marrying him. Alanna had never had any time for Rolt and she had not intention of making her marriage a real one — yet how could she explain this unwilling attraction she kept feeling for her husband?

A MAN TO BE FEARED
by Anne Hampson

Juliet had hated Dorian Coralis for years, for the hurt and humiliation he had caused her. Now she had her chance of revenge. She had planned it all for so long…and then, with success in her grasp, she found the whole thing going disastrously wrong.

Mills & Boon
the rose of romance

Best Seller Romances

Next month's best loved romances

Mills & Boon Best Seller Romances are the love stories that have proved particularly popular with our readers. These are the titles to look out for next month.

ADAM'S BRIDE
Rosemary Carter

THE DEVIL AT ARCHANGEL
Sara Craven

SONORA SUNDOWN
Janet Dailey

UNWANTED WIFE
Rachel Lindsay

Buy them from your usual paperback stockist, or write to: Mills & Boon Reader Service, P.O. Box 236, Thornton Rd, Croydon, Surrey CR9 3RU, England. Readers in South Africa-write to: Mills & Boon Reader Service of Southern Africa, Private Bag X3010, Randburg, 2125.

Mills & Boon
the rose of romance

Mills & Boon

Accept 4
Best Selling Romances
Absolutely
FREE

Enjoy the very best of love, romance and intrigue brought to you by Mills & Boon. Every month Mills & Boon very carefully select 4 Romances that have been particularly popular in the past and re-issue them for the benefit of readers who may have missed them first time round. Become a subscriber and you can receive all 4 superb novels every month, and your personal membership card will entitle you to a whole range of special benefits too: a free monthly newsletter, packed with exclusive book offers, recipes, competitions and your guide to the stars, plus there are other bargain offers and big cash savings.

AND an Introductory FREE GIFT for YOU.
Turn over the page for details.

As a special introduction we will send you
FOUR superb and exciting
Best Seller Romances – yours to keep Free
– when you complete and return
this coupon to us.

At the same time we will reserve a
subscription to Mills & Boon Best Seller
Romances for you. Every month you will
receive the 4 specially selected Best Seller
novels delivered direct to your door. Postage
and packing is always completely Free.
There is no obligation or commitment -
you can cancel your subscription
at any time.

You have absolutely nothing to lose and a whole world of
romance to gain. Simply fill in and post the coupon today to:-
MILLS & BOON READER SERVICE, FREEPOST,
P.O. BOX 236, CROYDON, SURREY CR9 9EL.

Please note:- READERS IN SOUTH AFRICA write to
Mills & Boon Ltd., Postbag X3010,
Randburg 2125, S. Africa.

- -

FREE BOOKS CERTIFICATE

**To: Mills & Boon Reader Service, FREEPOST, P.O. Box 236,
Croydon, Surrey CR9 9EL.**

Please send me, free and without obligation, four Mills & Boon Best Seller Romances, &
reserve a Reader Service Subscription for me. If I decide to subscribe I shall receive four new
books each month for £4.00, post and packing free. If I decide not to subscribe, I shall write
to you within 10 days. The free books are mine to keep in any case. I understand that I may
cancel my subscription at any time simply by writing to you. I am over 18 years of age.
Please write in BLOCK CAPITALS.

Name _____

Address _____

_____

_____ Postcode _____

SEND NO MONEY — TAKE NO RISKS.

*Remember, postcodes speed delivery. Offer applies in UK only and is not valid to
present subscribers. Mills & Boon reserve the right to exercise discretion
in granting membership. If price changes are necessary you will be noti-
fied. Offer expires 31st December 1984.*

4BS

EP10